Integrated Vocabulary Development

Book B

by
Donn Mosenfelder

EDUCATIONAL DESIGN, INC.
EDI 316

ISBN# 0-87694-066-1   EDI 316

Table of Contents

TO THE STUDENT:

You probably already have at least some understanding of a great many words taught in this book. Nontheless, the lessons that follow will help you increase your vocabulary by a considerable amount.

First of all, you will learn many words you do not know. Secondly, you will gain a better understanding of the words you already have some knowledge of.

Words have different meanings depending upon how they are used. Each of the words taught in this course is presented and tested in several different contexts, and the contexts vary. Sometimes the resulting differences in meaning are slight. Sometimes they are considerable.

The types of questions used also vary. Among the different types of answers you are asked to find are—

- Words with the same meanings (synonyms).
- Words with different meanings (antonyms).
- Answers to "fill in the blank" questions.
- Answers to questions about the meanings of words.
- Definitions for you to figure out from the contexts in which words are presented.
- The meanings of prefixes.
- Analogies, that is, pairs of words that have similar relationships to the relationships in other pairs of words.

The antonym questions are often difficult. Be especially careful with these. The analogy questions are even more difficult. Lesson G in Chapter 1 will help you understand this type of question better.

Turn the page and begin. You may want to read over the list of words in the chapter before you begin Lesson A.

CHAPTER 1.

Words in this chapter:

ailment
alcoholic
anthem
appliance
attachment

belfry
blemish

carburetor
clearance
columnist

depression
donor
drunkard

enclosure
era

gadget

homicide
horsepower
humanity

illegal
immigration
imperfect
improper

impurity
incapable
inquiry

juror

lubricant

maroon
massacre
monastery

ointment

piston
plaque
postscript
propaganda
proprietor

realm

sheath
soprano
stanza
stratosphere

transmission
transplant

vacancy

A. Nouns with Simple Definitions

ailment	sickness
belfry	a bell tower
donor	giver
gadget	a simple machine
homicide	killing of a person
juror	a member of a jury
maroon	a dark red color
monastery	a place that houses monks
soprano	a very high woman's singing voice
stanza	a group of lines in a poem

(1–5) Choose the word or phrase with the **same** meaning, or almost the same meaning, as the word in bold type.

1. the last *stanza* in the poem

   A. meaning   C. verse
   B. rhyme   D. word

2. the victim of a *homicide*

   A. attack   C. murder
   B. false accusation   D. theft

3. a rare *ailment*

   A. find   C. result
   B. illness   D. work of art

4. a generous *donor*

   A. contributor   C. gift
   B. friend   D. politician

5. a complicated *gadget*

   A. device   C. sentence
   B. plan   D. thought

(6–10) Answer the following questions.

6. When someone says you have "bats in your belfry," it means you are a little crazy. In this expression, *belfry* refers to your

   A. feet   C. head
   B. hands   D. stomach

7. Where might you find a *soprano*?

   A. car   C. newspaper
   B. choir   D. supermarket

8. What does a *juror* do?

   A. decides whether or not a person is guilty
   B. repairs aircraft engines
   C. travels in style
   D. writes poetry

9. What activity do you think of when you think of a **monastery**?

   A. big business deal   C. prayer

   B. championship football game   D. shooting a gun

10. Which of the following is likely to be **maroon** in color?

    A. a rose   C. the moon

    B. grass   D. the sea

(11–15) Fill in the missing word in the sentence.

11. When Jackie had her operation, I offered to be a blood _____.

    A. ailment   C. juror

    B. donor   D. soprano

12. Harold, you can't be a(n) _____! You're a man!

    A. ailment   C. juror

    B. donor   D. soprano

13. Elaine invented a new _____ to help pick fleas off the dog.

    A. belfry   C. monastery

    B. gadget   D. stanza

14. Do you notice that he always gets the first and third lines in the _____ to rhyme?

    A. belfry   C. monastery

    B. gadget   D. stanza

15. Joey is a detective who has the assignment of investigating _____.

    A. homicides   C. maroons

    B. jurors   D. sopranos

B. Nouns with Longer Definitions

anthem   A sacred song. Also, the official song of a country, such as "The Star Spangled Banner."

appliance   A stove or refrigerator or the like. Also, more generally, a tool or device.

columnist   A person who writes newspaper or magazine articles on a regular basis.

immigration   Coming into a new country and settling there.

ointment   A salve, a healing substance you rub on your skin—for burns, cuts, sores, itches, and so on.

propaganda   Phony or misleading information or phony news, the type of information some governments spread to deceive their populations.

sheath   A case for a knife, or a covering for a plant or body part, or more generally, any covering.

stratosphere   Upper part of the atmosphere, beginning about 7 miles above the earth.

6

transplant   A plant which has been moved to new soil. Or (in medicine) a healthy organ (often from a dead person's body) which has been implanted into a person's body to replace a sick organ. Also, *[verb]* to carry out such an operation, or to move a plant to new soil, or in general, to move from one area to another.

vacancy   An unfilled position (such as a political office or a job in a company). Also, a house or apartment which is up for rent.

(1–5) Choose the word or phrase with the **same** meaning, or almost the same meaning, as the word in bold type.

1. bought a new *appliance*

   A. bicycle   C. sofa
   B. diamond ring   D. washing machine

2. filled with *propaganda*

   A. fascinating   C. mathematical
       stories   formulas
   B. falsehoods   D. names of famous
                       people

3. we have a *vacancy*

   A. prize   C. unoccupied dwelling
   B. problem   D. very intelligent child

4. a sports *columnist*

   A. coach   C. fan
   B. competitor   D. writer

5. *sheath* of a sword

   A. blade   C. holder
   B. handle   D. tip

(6–8) Choose the word or phrase with the **opposite** meaning, or with the meaning which is most nearly opposite.

6. flew in the *stratosphere*

   A. air near the   C. clear skies
       ground
   B. below deck   D. outside

7. need to *transplant* those roses

   A. cut them back C. give them away
   B. dry them out   D. leave them where
                      they are

8. the laws about *immigration*

   A. closing a   C. receiving tax
       business   benefits
   B. divorce   D. staying in your own
                     country

(9–10) Answer the following questions.

9. Which of the following is an *ointment*?

   A. aspirin   C. salt
   B. facial cream   D. toothpaste

10. A national *anthem* is

   A. a flag   C. a musical piece
   B. a governmental D. the country's
       body   boundaries

(11–15) Fill in the missing word in the sentence.

11. The woman who writes *Dear Abby* is a ter-
   rific _____. I read her every
   day.

   A. anthem   C. propaganda
   B. columnist   D. trance

12. My little sister smeared mother's burn
   _____ all over her face.

   A. appliance   C. sheath
   B. ointment   D. trance

13. We had been driving for 10 hours, and we were dead tired. But all the motels had "no _____" signs.

    A. immigration   C. stratosphere

    B. propaganda   D. vacancy

14. When they played the National _____, all the soldiers stood up and saluted.

    A. Anthem   C. Propaganda

    B. Immigration   D. Trance

15. Dishwashers are expensive _____.

    A. appliances   C. sheaths

    B. ointments   D. stratospheres

C. Definitions for You to Derive from Context

Read the sentence following the word in bold type and on the basis of what you read, choose the correct definition.

1. **alcoholic**
You may think you just drink for fun, but when you get drunk almost every night, it's clear you are an *alcoholic*.

    A. a person who gets drunk regularly   C. a person who makes drinks

    B. a person who knows how to have fun   D. a person who sells drinks

2. What kinds of drinks does an *alcoholic* consume?

    A. beer, wine, and whiskey   C. milk

    B. juice   D. soda

3. **blemish**
He let me have the shirt for half price because there was a small *blemish* on the collar.

    A. button   C. hanger

    B. defect   D. button

4. Which of the following is a skin *blemish*?

    A. eyelid   C. scar

    B. hair   D. suntan

5. **drunkard**
Sarah drinks all the time. She's a terrible *drunkard*.

    A. alcoholic   C. player

    B. companion   D. worker

6. Which of the following is a common characteristic of *drunkards*?

    A. bad breath   C. great wealth

    B. fast feet   D. strong will

7. **enclosure**
I suggest you put a fence around that field to make it into an *enclosure*.

    A. closed-in area   C. hill

    B. forest   D. swampy land

8. opposite of *enclosure*

    A. air   C. sea

    B. open land   D. street

9. **era**
I wouldn't call the month or so you have been president an "*era*." It's not long enough.

    A. beginning   C. major time period

    B. cause   D. success

10. Which of the following might be called an *era*?

  A. the Age of Reptiles
  B. the first rocket flight to the moon
  C. the time school lets out
  D. your birthday

11. **inquiry**

  I received an *inquiry* from the school, asking for information about John.

  A. bank check
  B. medal
  C. report card
  D. request for information

12. If you make an *inquiry* into a situation, you

  A. help it along
  B. investigate it
  C. join it
  D. spend money on it

13. **massacre**

  It was a *massacre*. Hundreds of people had been murdered.

  A. cheating
  B. discovery
  C. slaughter of many people
  D. theatrical production

14. Where do *massacres* most frequently occur?

  A. at supper
  B. at work
  C. in war
  D. in your mind

15. **postscript**

  I signed the letter to Amanda. Then I added a *postscript* at the bottom of the page, telling her about the news from Gloria.

  A. address
  B. date
  C. note at the bottom of a letter
  D. stamp

16. *Script* is a form of the Latin word for "write." What do you think the prefix *post-* means?

  A. before
  B. during
  C. after

17. **proprietor**

  I don't want to speak to an employee. I want to speak to the *proprietor*.

  A. customer
  B. hired hand
  C. neighbor
  D. owner

18. Sal built the apartment house. Enrico is the real estate agent who sold it for him. Melinda bought it. Grace rents an apartment in it. Who is the *proprietor*?

  A. Sal
  B. Enrico
  C. Melinda
  D. Grace

19. **realm**

  The king's *realm* stretched for hundreds of miles in all directions.

  A. court
  B. crown
  C. kingdom
  D. queen

20. Which of the following might be considered a *realm*?

  A. a football field
  B. a highway
  C. the United Kingdom
  D. your back yard

D. Nouns for You to Look Up in the Dictionary

(1–5) Each of the nouns in bold type has to do with cars, at least in part of its definition. Unless you are sure you know the word's meaning, look it up. Then choose the word or phrase with a similar meaning.

1. a problem with the *carburetor*

   A. a motor-cooling device
   B. part of the engine that mixes gas and air
   C. the car's electrical system
   D. the shaft that transmits power to the wheels

2. how many *horsepower*?

   A. unit of gas consumption
   B. unit of power
   C. unit of size
   D. unit of speed

3. a motor *lubricant*

   A. bolt
   B. oil
   C. repair
   D. starting device

4. blew a *piston*

   A. electrical switch
   B. gear shaft
   C. sliding metal piece
   D. valve that lets the gas in

5. faulty *transmission*

   A. exhaust system
   B. gearbox
   C. radiator
   D. spark plugs

(6–8) Answer the following questions.

6. In general, a *lubricant* is any kind of substance that lets things

   A. burn hotter
   B. rub together
   C. start up in cold weather

7. *Transmission* comes from the word *transmit*, which means

   A. break
   B. hold
   C. send
   D. stop

8. One *horsepower* is roughly equal to the amount of power

   A. a car has on the open road
   B. an engine has when it starts up
   C. a horse exerts in pulling

(9–10) Fill in the missing word in the sentence.

9. The mechanic adjusted the _____ to let more air in.

   A. carburetor
   B. horsepower
   C. piston
   D. transmission

10. The _____ move up and down in a metal cylinder.

    A. carburetors
    B. horsepowers
    C. pistons
    D. transmissions

E. Nouns with More than One Meaning

All the words in this lesson are nouns which have more than one common meaning.

attachment   a. Strong liking for another person.

b. Something you can attach to another thing.

clearance   a. Official permission.

b. A store sale, to get rid of goods.

c. The distance which one object needs to *clear*, or get past another. *Clearance* is important for trucks passing under bridges or tunnel entrances, or for objects being brought through a doorway.

depression   a. State of feeling very sad.

b. A period when the economy is doing badly.

c. A low place in the landscape.

d. In general, any weighing down or lowering.

humanity   a. People, in general.

b. The quality of being a human being, that is, of being a decent person.

c. (used in the plural—*humanities*) Such school subjects as English, literature, art, and philosophy—the subjects that teach people about books and the history of thought.

plaque   a. A flat piece of metal, wood, or plastic with writing on it, usually to describe the object the *plaque* is attached to.

b. A film of germs on the teeth. One of the main reasons you brush your teeth is to get rid of *plaque*.

(1–2) Choose the word or phrase with the **same** meaning, or almost the same meaning, as the word in bold type.

1. official government *clearance*

    A. approval   C. program
    B. position   D. refusal

2. read the *plaque*

    A. holy writing   C. story to be made into a play
    B. instructions for use   D. tablet with writing on it

(3–5) Choose the word or phrase with the **opposite** meaning, or with the meaning which is most nearly opposite.

3. show his *humanity*

    A. funny feeling   C. lack of skill
    B. generosity   D. nastiness

4. a strong *attachment*

    A. decline   C. following
    B. dislike   D. recovery

5. going into a *depression*
   - A. boom in the economy
   - B. darkened room
   - C. large area
   - D. slow walk

(6–8) Fill in the missing word in the sentence.

6. After her father died, Gloria went into a terible state of _____.
   - A. attachment
   - B. clearance
   - C. depression
   - D. humanity

7. The dentist said I needed a good cleaning to get rid of the _____ on my teeth.
   - A. attachment
   - B. clearance
   - C. humanity
   - D. plaque

8. The _____ for the vacuum cleaner all fit inside the top part of the machine.
   - A. attachments
   - B. clearances
   - C. depressions
   - D. plaques

(9–10) Pick out the best sentence to go with the definition.

9. a period when the economy is doing badly
   - A. During the Great *Depression*, many banks failed.
   - B. Many doctors treat *depression* with drugs.
   - C. You can't see the cowboys in the distance right now because they're riding through a *depression* in the landscape.

10. a store sale
   - A. Mallory's is having a *clearance* on tennis rackets this Saturday and Sunday.
   - B. Selene has top secret *clearance* for her Air Force job.
   - C. This tunnel has a *clearance* of 10 feet 3 inches.

F. Words with the Prefix *In-*, "Not"

The prefix *in-* has two very different meanings, "not" and "in." When *in-* is found at the beginning of an adjective, the "not" meaning is the more probable one.

In- can also be spelled *il-*, *im-*, and *ir-*, depending on the consonant that follows it.

illegal   [*adjective*] Not legal.

imperfect   [*adjective*] Not perfect.

improper   [*adjective*] Not proper.

impurity   [*noun*] Something that is not pure, something that doesn't belong.

incapable   [*adjective*] Not able to do something.

(1–2) Choose the word or phrase with the **same** meaning, or almost the same meaning, as the word in bold type.

1. an *impurity* in the water

   A. drowning   C. high temperature

   B. foreign   D. reflection
   substance

2. an *illegal* act

   A. amusing   C. difficult

   B. criminal   D. ugly

(3–5) Choose the word or phrase with the **opposite** meaning, or with the meaning which is most nearly opposite.

3. with *imperfect* results

   A. flawless   C. rewarding

   B. memorable   D. strange

4. *improper* behavior

   A. angry   C. correct

   B. childish   D. crazy

5. *incapable* of winning

   A. afraid   C. hopeful

   B. having the   D. used to
   ability

(6–8) Fill in the missing word in the sentence.

6. It is _____ to drive your car without a license.

   A. illegal   C. impurity

   B. imperfect   D. incapable

7. I don't love Ricardo anymore because he is _____ of showing affection.

   A. illegal   C. improper

   B. imperfect   D. incapable

8. It is _____ of you to dress like a bum when we are going to supper with your grandparents.

   A. illegal   C. improper

   B. imperfect   D. incapable

(9–10) Answer the following questions.

9. Which word is closest in meaning to *illegal*?

   A. imperfect   C. impurity

   B. improper   D. incapable

10. When *impurities* are found in diamonds, what is the result?

    A. less valuable

    B. more valuable

G. Analogies

In this lesson you will use some of the words you have learned in the present chapter to improve your skill at identifying *analogies*.

When you are asked to pick out an analogy, you are expected to choose a pair of words that has the same relationship, or the most similar relationship, one word to the other, as another pair of words. For example, a *dog* makes a *bark*, just as a *cat* makes a *meow*. *Dog : bark* is an analogy of *cat : meow*.

Analogy questions can be difficult. To improve your skill at identifying analogies, work through the exercises below. The first four questions ask you to identify similarities, which is the most important thing you have to do to pick out analogies.

(1–2) Fill in the missing word in the sentence.

1. **Soldiers** live in **barracks**, just as _____ live in **monasteries**.

   A. athletes   C. monks
   B. generals   D. prisoners

2. A **postscript** comes at the end of a **letter**, just as a _____ comes at the end of a **sentence**.

   A. message   C. verb
   B. period   D. writer

(3–4) Answer the following questions.

3. A **poet** writes **poems**, just as a **columnist**

   A. has to be good at writing
   B. works for a newspaper
   C. writes newspaper articles

4. An **appliance** runs on **electricity**, just as

   A. a car runs on gas
   B. a fire can burn wood
   C. a house has a front door

(5–7) Look carefully at the pairs of words in capitals. Try to figure out the relationship between each pair. Then choose the sentence that does the **best** job of showing how the words are related.

5. SHEATH : KNIFE

   A. A knife can cut a hole in a sheath.
   B. A sheath is like a knife.
   C. A sheath is used to hold a knife.

6. PROPRIETOR : BUSINESS

   A. A proprietor is the boss of a business.
   B. A proprietor likes business.
   C. A proprietor works for a business.

7. DRUNKARD : ALCOHOLIC

   A. A drunkard is likely to enjoy the company of an alcoholic.
   B. A drunkard understands an alcoholic.
   C. "Drunkard" means the same thing as "alcoholic."

(8–10) Figure out how the first two words in capitals are related to each other. Then choose the pair of words below it that are related in the same way.

8. SHEATH : KNIFE

   A. BAG : BROWN
   B. BAG : GROCERIES
   C. BAG : PAPER

9. PROPRIETOR : BUSINESS

   A. CEMENT : BASEMENT
   B. MANAGER : TEAM
   C. STUDENT : SCHOOL

10. DRUNKARD : ALCOHOLIC

   A. MOTHER : CHILD
   B. PRIEST : RELIGION
   C. WORKER : EMPLOYEE

H. Chapter 1 Review

(1–7) Choose the word or phrase with the **same** meaning, or almost the same meaning, as the word in bold type.

1. time to *transplant* the shrubs

   A. feed
   B. move to new soil
   C. start growing
   D. trim

2. suffering from *depression*

   A. bruises
   B. high temperatures
   C. infection
   D. sad feelings

3. our *humanities* classes

   A. English, art, and philosophy
   B. psychology and sociology
   C. physics and chemistry
   D. studies of the human body

4. able to reach the *stratosphere*

   A. feelings of contentment
   B. highest point
   C. stars
   D. upper part of the atmosphere

5. *immigration* laws

   A. having to do with alcohol and drugs
   B. having to do with marriage and divorce
   C. having to do with people entering the country
   D. having to do with protection of the environment

6. formed an *attachment*

   A. group
   B. opinion
   C. plan
   D. strong liking

7. an *imperfect* record

   A. dependable
   B. hard to beat
   C. not perfect
   D. temporary

(8–12) Choose the word or phrase with the **opposite** meaning, or with the meaning which is most nearly opposite.

8. a *vacancy* in the company

   A. filled position
   B. finished task
   C. high-level job
   D. spelled-out procedure

9. guilty of *homicide*

   A. being too generous
   B. reporting a crime
   C. returning money
   D. saving a life

10. a new kind of *ailment*

    A. finished report
    B. growth
    C. healthy condition
    D. success

11. has made it *illegal*

    A. contented
    B. free
    C. lawful
    D. visible

12. get rid of all the *impurities*

    A. good laws
    B. new findings
    C. smart people
    D. things that belong

(13–17) Fill in the missing word in the sentence.

13. The motor is missing, but all you probably need is a _____ adjustment.

    A. carburetor
    B. horsepower
    C. piston
    D. transmission

14. She has a(n) _____ voice.

    A. anthem
    B. clearance
    C. maroon
    D. soprano

15. My father was a(n) _____ for the *Philadelphia Inquirer* newspaper.

 A. appliance C. donor
 B. columnist D. juror

16. Did you read the _____ at the bottom of the letter?

 A. inquiry C. propaganda
 B. postscript D. stanza

17. The dentist removed _____ from my teeth.

 A. blemishes C. lubricants
 B. enclosures D. plaque

(18–19) Choose the word that has the two meanings that are in bold type.

18. *official permission; store sale*

 A. authorization C. discount
 B. clearance D. sanction

19. *germs on the teeth; badge*

 A. cavities C. plaque
 B. inscription D. tablet

(20) Pick out the best sentence to go with the definition.

20. period when the economy is doing badly

 A. Can you see those three cows? You can just see their heads above the *depression* in the landscape.
 B. Enrico suffers from fits of *depression*.
 C. That bridge was built during the Great *Depression*.

(21) Answer the following question.

21. What does the prefix *im-* in *improper* mean?

 A. against C. not
 B. into D. with

(22–23) Look carefully at the pairs of words in capitals. Try to figure out the relationship between each pair. Then choose the sentence that does the **best** job of showing how the words are related.

22. CHURCH : BELFRY

 A. A church and a belfry can both be made of stone.
 B. A church is made more beautiful by a belfry.
 C. At the top of a church is a belfry.

23. DEPRESSION : HAPPINESS

 A. A depression can lead to happiness.
 B. A depression is not as common as happiness.
 C. A mood of depression is the opposite of happiness.

(24–25) Figure out how the first two words in capitals are related to each other. Then choose the pair of words below it that are related in the same way.

24. CHURCH : BELFRY

 A. CAR : GASOLINE
 B. HOUSE : ATTIC
 C. TREE : SHRUB

25. DEPRESSION : HAPPINESS

 A. NOSE : SMELL
 B. POOR : RICH
 C. TOE : FOOT

CHAPTER 2.

Words in this chapter:

admirable

advisable

ample

anatomy

attentive

authentic

colossal

delirious

dental

dingy

energetic

envious

external

extinct

faulty

flexible

fossil

heredity

honorary

hospitable

humane

identical

impressive

inflammable

inflict

inlaid

inscription

intrude

invasion

invert

logical

miscellaneous

molecule

negative

noticeable

oblong

perpendicular

physics

precise

sensitive

singular

solitary

strenuous

superb

vocal

A. Adjectives with Simple Definitions

advisable	recommended
ample	plentiful, in good supply
authentic	genuine
colossal	huge
dental	of the teeth
external	on the outside or coming from the outside
faulty	not working properly
miscellaneous	consisting of a mixture of things
precise	exact
solitary	single, alone

(1–5) Choose the word or phrase with the **same** meaning, or almost the same meaning, as the word in bold type.

1. **miscellaneous** things for sale

   A. assorted   C. suitable
   B. inexpensive   D. worthless

2. an **advisable** course of action

   A. boring   C. difficult
   B. careful   D. wise

3. **ample** reasons

   A. negative   C. sufficient
   B. possible   D. well-thought-out

4. a **solitary** man

   A. intelligent   C. strong
   B. lonely   D. wicked

5. **dental** cream

   A. athlete's foot C. half-and-half
   B. facial   D. toothpaste

(6–10) Choose the word or phrase with the **opposite** meaning, or with the meaning which is most nearly opposite.

6. a **faulty** motor

   A. ancient   C. powerful
   B. perfect   D. unreliable

7. a **colossal** tower

   A. high   C. tiny
   B. strong   D. ugly

8. **external** pressures

   A. avoidable   C. fake
   B. body   D. inner

9. **precise** directions

   A. final   C. inaccurate
   B. forgotten   D. lengthy

10. **authentic** Italian cooking

    A. fake   C. southern
    B. hard-to-recog- D. tasty
       nize

(11–15) Fill in the missing word in the sentence.

11. The prisoner was placed in _____ confinement in a tiny cell without any windows.

    A. ample   C. internal
    B. authentic   D. solitary

12. Next time, it would be _____ for you to get your paper in on time.

    A. advisable   C. faulty
    B. authentic   D. precise

13. First they gave us nouns, then adjectives, then verbs, and then a(n) _____ section with some of each.

    A. ample   C. miscellaneous
    B. colossal   D. precise

14. Our new health insurance plan has both medical and _____ benefits.

    A. dental   C. miscellaneous
    B. faulty   D. precise

15. Jones has made a lot of simple mistakes, but this one is a(n) _____ blunder.

    A. advisable   C. colossal
    B. ample   D. external

B. Adjectives with Longer Definitions

attentive	Thoughtful, paying attention to other people's needs or to what is needed.
delirious	Mentally very disturbed and very confused, unable to understand what is going on and sometimes having strange and unreal thoughts. A *delirious* person is sometimes very excited and talks wildly without making sense.
extinct	No longer burning (a fire) or no longer existing (such as animals of a particular kind that have all died out).
hospitable	Very friendly and generous in the way you welcome people, particularly guests.
humane	Very thoughtful and helpful to other people or to animals, trying to keep them from any suffering. Do *not* confuse with *human*, without the *e* on the end, meaning "having to do with men and women, as opposed to other animals."
inlaid	Set into the surface, particularly as regards decorative work in such things as furniture and floors.
oblong	Stretched out in shape, of greater length than width, particularly in a four-sided figure with square corners. Also, [*noun*] an object having an *oblong* shape.
perpendicular	Rising straight up in the air. Or, in math, describing a line that is at right angles to another line, even if it doesn't rise straight up in the air (it could go sideways or downward). Also, [*noun*] a *perpendicular* line.

singular   ·Individual, having to do with only one person, or one event, or one thing, etc. Also, more generally, exceptional, different, of unusual quality.

strenuous   Very active, vigorous. Or requiring great effort, and therefore difficult and tiring.

(1–5) Choose the word or phrase with the **same** meaning, or almost the same meaning, as the word in bold type.

1. a **delirious** patient

   A. crazy
   B. former
   C. recovering
   D. with cancer

2. in the shape of an **oblong**

   A. figure looking like a house
   B. circle
   C. streamlined design
   D. triangle

3. **perpendicular** to the Earth's surface

   A. along the horizon
   B. attached
   C. sinking
   D. vertical

4. an **inlaid** wood table design

   A. bent
   B. highly polished
   C. made of different kinds of wood
   D. painted

5. in the **singular**

   A. future
   B. not plural
   C. popular
   D. unimportant

(6–10) Choose the word or phrase with the **opposite** meaning, or with the meaning which is most nearly opposite.

6. **strenuous** exercise

   A. desirable
   B. easy
   C. impossible
   D. irregular

7. **attentive to** your instructions

   A. adding suggestions
   B. criticizing
   C. not listening to
   D. repeating

8. **humane** treatment

   A. cruel
   B. stuffy
   C. stupid
   D. wild

9. **hospitable** service

   A. dangerous to your health
   B. not asked for
   C. underpaid
   D. unfriendly

10. an **extinct** type of bird

    A. alive
    B. low-flying
    C. tame
    D. vegetable-eating

(11–15) Fill in the missing word in the sentence.

11. I called the _____ Society to come pick up the poor little stray dog that had been hit by a car.

    A. Attentive
    B. Hospital
    C. Humane
    D. Singular

12. A 35-mile bike ride may be too _____ for people of your age.

    A. delirious
    B. extinct
    C. hospitable
    D. strenuous

13. Run a(n) _____ line running from Point A to Line X.

    A. inlaid
    B. oblong
    C. perpendicular
    D. singular

14. I have never been so sick and feverish. They tell me I was _____ for almost four whole days.

    A. attentive
    B. delirious
    C. extinct
    D. hospitable

15. There are very few grizzly bears left in the world. In a few years, they may become _____.

    A. extinct   C. inlaid
    B. humane   D. oblong

C. Definitions for You to Derive from Context

Read the sentence following the word in bold type and on the basis of what you read, choose the correct definition.

1. **admirable**
   The paper you wrote for class is an excellent paper, *admirable* in every respect!

   A. beginning   C. unheard of
   B. copied   D. very fine

2. opposite of *admirable*

   A. expensive   C. not worthwhile
   B. final   D. stiff

3. **dingy**
   You're lucky to have this apartment. At least it's clean and it's got enough room to move around in. You should see the *dingy* place I have.

   A. expensive   C. on a high floor
   B. new   D. small and crowded

4. Which is most likely to be *dingy*?

   A. blue skies   C. cowboy country
   B. cell in a prison D. king's castle

5. **energetic**
   My brother is so *energetic*. He gets up early every morning and runs three miles. Then he bikes to school.

   A. angry   C. dangerous
   B. childish   D. vigorous

6. The word *energetic* is derived from the word

   A. energy   C. net
   B. get   D. regret

7. **envious**
   Sarah is *envious* of me because I got the best grade in the class. She always feels she's competing with me.

   A. afraid   C. aware
   B. ahead   D. jealous

8. *Envious* people want

   A. only what is fair C. what other people have
   B. very little   D. what they have always had

9. **honorary**
   Jan has received an *honorary* award in recognition of all of her years of service to the local citizens' group.

   A. chance   C. local
   B. given in   D. rejected
      honor of

10. An *honorary* title is

    A. an insult   C. given to everyone
    B. easily   D. one you can be
       purchased   proud of

11. **identical**
    There are two kinds of twins. Fraternal twins are born at the same time but can be quite different. *Identical* twins are so much alike you have a hard time telling them apart.

    A. exactly alike   C. joined together
    B. identifiable   D. tiny at birth

12. opposite of *identical*
    A. alive   C. eager
    B. different   D. manufactured

13. **impressive**
    She may have *impressive* grades, but she doesn't impress me in other ways.
    A. end-of-year   C. kept secret
    B. high school   D. worthy of notice

14. opposite of *impressive*
    A. expanded   C. insignificant
    B. faulty   D. revised

15. **logical**
    That's the *logical* way of doing it, but instead we always seem to do things in ways that don't make sense.
    A. actual   C. difficult
    B. different   D. sensible

16. How do you arrive at a *logical* conclusion?
    A. by chance   C. by not interfering
    B. by hurrying to   D. by reasoning
    the end

17. **noticeable**
    I don't know why you didn't take notice of that beautiful woman in the red dress. She was certainly *noticeable* enough.
    A. from the neigh-   C. skinny
    borhood
    B. intelligent   D. worthy of attention

18. opposite of *noticeable*
    A. hard to pick out   C. ripe
    B. loud   D. tasteless

19. **superb**
    This meal is absolutely *superb*. Nothing could be fresher, tastier, or better in any way.
    A. cooked   C. the finest
    B. eaten   D. wasted

20. *Superb* describes
    A. zero   C. better
    B. good   D. best

D. Words for You to Look Up in the Dictionary

(1–5) Each of the words in bold type has to do with various kinds of science. Unless you are sure you know the word's meaning, look it up. Then choose the word or phrase with a similar meaning.

1. *anatomy* lessons
   A. the study of the   C. the study of the
   building blocks   moon and the stars
   of matter
   B. the study of the   D. the study of the
   forces of nature   parts of living plants
   and animals

2. the *fossil* record
   A. measure of   C. scientific proof
   noise levels
   B. remains of   D. study of growth
   ancient plants   patterns
   and animals

3. a matter of *heredity*
   A. chemical   C. qualities passed
   process   from one generation
   to another
   B. measure of   D. way food is used by
   force and energy   the body

4. a carbon **molecule**

   A. basic building   C. energy bond
     block of matter

   B. chemical com-   D. substance made in
     bination   a science lab

5. student of **physics**

   A. study of living   C. study of rocks
     matter

   B. study of natural   D. study of the bones
     science   of the body

(6–8) Answer the following questions.

6. Your **heredity** tells

   A. the qualities you were born with

   B. the qualities you have developed in life

7. What are **fossils** usually made of?

   A. paper   C. wood
   B. rock   D. many different
                things

8. All **molecules** are

   A. very bright   C. very simple
   B. very heavy   D. very small

(9–10) Fill in the missing word in the sentence.

9. The study of such things as matter, force, and energy is part of _____.

   A. anatomy   C. physics
   B. heredity

10. The study of the organs of the body is part of _____.

   A. anatomy   C. physics
   B. heredity

E. Adjectives with More than One Meaning

All the words in this lesson are adjectives with more than one meaning.

flexible
  a. Capable of stretching and bending easily.
  b. Willing to compromise (that is, willing to bend).

inflammable
  a. Easily set on fire. (Strangely, **flammable** means the same thing.)
  b. Easily excited or angered (that is, easily brought to the point of fiery anger).

negative
  a. Opposed to. The opposite of positive. Not positive.
  b. In math, less than zero (as opposed to "positive" quantities, which are more than zero).
  c. In electricity, having to do with one of the two directions in the flow of current ("**negative**" as opposed to "positive").

sensitive
  a. Easily hurt or easily upset.
  b. Capable of noticing or being changed by or responding to even the slightest things.
  c. Capable of responding to artistic things.

vocal
  a. Spoken or sung.
  b. Strongly expressed.

(1–3) Choose the word or phrase with the **same** meaning, or almost the same meaning, as the word in bold type.

1. a *negative* personality

   A. constantly changing
   B. difficult to describe
   C. disagreeable
   D. uncontrolled

2. *flexible* back muscles

   A. bulging
   B. damaged
   C. elastic
   D. growing

3. *vocal* chords

   A. easily seen
   B. feeble
   C. twisted
   D. voice

(4–7) Choose the word or phrase with the **opposite** meaning, or with the meaning which is most nearly opposite.

4. a *sensitive* young man

   A. grown-up
   B. poorly educated
   C. stupid
   D. unfeeling

5. *inflammable* material

   A. fireproof
   B. heavy-duty
   C. machine-made
   D. stretchable

6. a *vocal* group of supporters

   A. dedicated
   B. ineffective
   C. numerous
   D. quiet

7. *flexible* demands

   A. reasonable
   B. unyielding
   C. weak
   D. written

(8) Pick out the best sentence to go with the definition.

8. a direction in the flow of current

   A. Hook that terminal up to the *negative* pole.
   B. Minus 3 is a *negative* number.
   C. Most people don't like what is going on, but they are afraid to express their *negative* feelings.

(9–10) Fill in the missing word in the sentence.

9. I told Alonso not to let that _____ temper of his get out of control.

   A. flexible
   B. inflammable
   C. sensitive
   D. vocal

10. Is your hearing _____ enough to make out all the different instruments on that new record?

   A. flexible
   B. inflammable
   C. sensitive
   D. vocal

F. Words with the Prefix *In-*, "Into"

The prefix *in-* often means "in," "into," or "on." Look out for its other forms: *il-*, *im-*, and *ir-*, depending on what consonant follows it.

inflict [*verb*] To lay something unpleasant on someone. You can *inflict* a blow, or a punishment, or a painful task. From *in-* + *flict*, a form of the Latin word meaning "to strike."

inscription [*noun*] A short written message on a book, painting, tombstone, gift, etc. From *in-* + *script*, a form of the Latin word meaning "to write."

intrude [*verb*] To butt in, to enter a place where you're not wanted. From *in-* + *trude*, a form of the Latin word meaning "to push."

invasion [*noun*] The attack on an area by a foreign army. Or, more generally, any entry or advance into a new area. From *in-* + *vade*, a form of the Latin word meaning "to go." When you *invade*, you go into another country.

invert [*verb*] To turn upside down or inside out, to reverse the order. From *in-* + *vert*, a form of the Latin word meaning "to turn." When you *invert* something, you turn it inward, that is, you change its order.

(1–3) Choose the word or phrase with the **same** meaning, or almost the same meaning, as the word in bold type.

1. the *inscription* at the bottom of the picture

   A. color   C. note
   B. frame   D. scene

2. to *inflict* a wound

   A. die from   C. heal
   B. feel   D. impose

3. prepare for the *invasion*

   A. attack   C. meeting
   B. game   D. test

(4–5) Choose the word or phrase with the **opposite** meaning, or with the meaning which is most nearly opposite.

4. in *inverted* order

   A. irregular   C. strange
   B. right-side-up   D. understandable

5. to *intrude on* a private conversation

   A. enter   C. listen to
   B. keep out of   D. take notes on

(6–8) Fill in the missing word in the sentence.

6. Can you make out the _____ on that gravestone? I think it says, "Beloved wife and mother."

   A. inflict   C. invasion
   B. inscription   D. invert

7. The German _____ of Russia began in the summer of 1941.

   A. inflict   C. intrude
   B. inscription   D. invasion

8. Why do you always _____ on things that don't concern you?

    A. inflict   C. invasion

    B. intrude   D. invert

(9–10) Answer the following questions.

9. If you **invert** the order of A,B, and C, what might you get?

    A. a,b,c   C. D,E,F

    B. C,B,A   D. zero

10. Something that has been **inflicted** upon you is

    A. something you wanted

    B. something you didn't want

G. Chapter 2 Review

(1–7) Choose the word or phrase with the **same** meaning, or almost the same meaning, as the word in bold type.

1. to be **precise**

    A. bold   C. generous

    B. exact   D. tired

2. **humane** actions

    A. alive   C. deliberate

    B. considerate   D. intelligent

3. **authentic** French cooking

    A. flavorful   C. overcooked

    B. genuine   D. rich

4. **external** parts of the house

    A. above the first floor   C. outside

    B. favorite   D. important

5. a **colossal** fortune

    A. growing   C. very large

    B. illegal   D. wasted

6. **faulty** parts

    A. difficult to obtain C. expensive

    B. dirty   D. not working properly

7. don't want to **intrude**

    A. butt in   C. do something foolish

    B. do harm to another person D. waste effort

(8–12) Choose the word or phrase with the **opposite** meaning, or with the meaning which is most nearly opposite.

8. the **logical** thing to do

    A. hopeful   C. necessary

    B. impolite   D. senseless

9. an **invasion** of ants

    A. departure   C. independent group

    B. harmless type D. small number

10. **ample** warning

    A. cheerful   C. loud

    B. insufficient   D. often repeated

11. a **superb** performance

    A. easily forgotten C. original

    B. enjoyable   D. terrible

12. an **energetic** saleswoman

    A. experienced   C. truthful

    B. lazy   D. unsuccessful

(13–17) Fill in the missing word in the sentence.

13. We began studying the muscles of the arm yesterday in our _____ classes.

    A. anatomy   C. heredity
    B. dental   D. molecule

14. Mt. Hood is a(n) _____ volcano. It hasn't erupted in thousands of years.

    A. delirious   C. extinct
    B. dingy   D. strenuous

15. The state university gave _____ degrees to the Vice President and the head of the United Nations.

    A. honorary   C. miscellaneous
    B. hospitable   D. singular

16. If you drop a ball, its fall is _____ to the earth's surface.

    A. identical   C. oblong
    B. inlaid   D. perpendicular

17. My brother is off in Wyoming digging up _____ of extinct dinosaurs.

    A. fossils   C. molecules
    B. inscriptions   D. physics

(18–19) Choose the word that has the two meanings that are in bold type.

18. *opposed to*; *less than zero*

    A. against   C. minus
    B. anti   D. negative

19. *spoken or sung*; *strongly expressed*

    A. expressive   C. outspoken
    B. oral   D. vocal

(20) Pick out the best sentence to go with the definition.

20. easily upset or hurt

    A. Maria is very **sensitive** to comments made about her brothers or sisters.
    B. Maria also has a **sensitive** eye for artistic things.
    C. The advantage of these new meters is that they are much more **sensitive** to even the slightest changes in temperature.

(21) Answer the following question.

21. What does the prefix **in-** in **intrude** mean?

    A. into   C. not
    B. made up of   D. opposite

(22–23) Look carefully at the pairs of words in capitals. Try to figure out the relationship between each pair. Then choose the sentence that does the **best** job of showing how the words are related.

22. FOSSILS : ROCK

    A. Fossils are usually lighter than rock.
    B. Fossils are usually made of rock.
    C. Fossils look different from rock.

23. IDENTICAL : SIMILAR

    A. Identical and similar mean the same.
    B. Identical means the opposite of similar.
    C. Things that are identical are more than similar.

(24–25) Figure out how the first two words in capitals are related to each other. Then choose the pair of words below it that are related in the same way.

24. FOSSILS : ROCK

    A. CHAIRS : WOOD

    B. SONGS : SINGER

    C. STORIES : WRITER

25. IDENTICAL : SIMILAR

    A. BEST : GOOD

    B. NOTHING : ZERO

    C. TINY : HUGE

CHAPTER 3.

Words in this chapter:

accessory
attorney

circuit
collision
communism
constable
currency

encounter
equality
exclamation
exclude
expectation
exquisite
extract

faculty
fixture
frill

intermission

juvenile

lecturer

mason
masterpiece
motive

nausea

option

pedestrian
plasma
portrait
projector
pulpit
pygmy

registration
rehearsal
renewal
respiration

Sabbath
salve
scandal
Scriptures
shortage
shrine

testament
trait

vat
verdict

A. Nouns with Simple Definitions

attorney	lawyer
collision	banging together
encounter	meeting
juvenile	a young person
lecturer	a person who gives lectures, a teacher
nausea	upset stomach
pedestrian	a person on foot, not in a car
plasma	the fluid part of blood
portrait	a picture of a person
respiration	breathing

(1–5) Choose the word or phrase with the **same** meaning, or almost the same meaning, as the word in bold type.

1. a fine *portrait*

   A. education   C. likeness
   B. food   D. speech

2. a brief *encounter*

   A. applause   C. message
   B. coming together   D. thought

3. considered a *juvenile*

   A. fine person   C. success
   B. good sport   D. youngster

4. a car *collision*

   A. accident   C. model
   B. license   D. motor part

5. listened to a *lecturer*

   A. politician   C. singer
   B. priest   D. speaker

(6–10) Answer the following questions.

6. What is most likely to give you *nausea*?

   A. a cold winter day   C. petting the dog
   B. a good grade   D. something you ate

7. When do people sometimes need *plasma*?

   A. after running a race   C. during an operation
   B. before church service   D. when they get up in the morning

8. When can an *attorney* help you?

   A. when you are feeling down   C. when you have legal problems
   B. when you are planning a trip   D. when you need money

9. Where do you often see *pedestrians*?

A. at work
B. in a swimming pool
C. on sidewalks
D. up in the air

10. What is the purpose of *respiration*?

A. to get air in your lungs
B. to rest up
C. to solve a problem
D. to tidy up the house

(11–15) Fill in the missing word in the sentence.

11. When you drive a car you should always remember that _____ have the right-of-way.

A. attorneys
B. juveniles
C. lecturers
D. pedestrians

12. Marie was sick of being treated like a(n) _____ by all her older cousins.

A. attorney
B. juvenile
C. lecturer
D. pedestrian

13. The word *encounter* has a little bit of the same meaning as _____.

A. collision
B. nausea
C. plasma
D. portrait

14. He painted a _____ of my mother that looks just like her.

A. collision
B. plasma
C. portrait
D. respiration

15. When I had the flu, I felt awful _____.

A. nausea
B. plasma
C. portrait
D. respiration

B. Nouns with Longer Definitions

accessory   Things of secondary importance. For example, wallets, belts, and key chains are *accessories* to your clothing. Also, a person who helps commit a crime, even if he or she is not the main criminal—and even if he or she is not present—is called an *accessory* to the crime.

communism   A system of government where the state owns all or most business, the type of government found in the Soviet Union.

constable   A policeman, particularly a British policeman.

fixture   Something fixed in place. We often talk of the *fixtures* of a house, such as the wall or ceiling lights, the doorbell—anything attached to the walls.

mason   A worker who is skilled at building with stone, brick, and so on.

projector   A device for showing movies, slides, etc., on a screen.

pygmy   A dwarf, particularly (capitalized), a member of a race of very short people in central Africa.

salve   An ointment, a healing substance you rub on your skin—for burns, cuts, sores, itches, and so on.

vat   A large tub, especially a tub used in the preparation of liquor or to hold dyes for dyeing clothes.

verdict   An opinion or decision, particularly the decision of a jury or judge in a law court.

(1–5) Choose the word or phrase with the **same** meaning, or almost the same meaning, as the word in bold type.

1. a *pygmy* in the forest
   - A. hunter
   - B. very small person
   - C. wild animal
   - D. young tree

2. fill up the *vat*
   - A. bank account
   - B. barrel
   - C. football stadium
   - D. refrigerator

3. *fixtures* in the sink
   - A. dirt
   - B. dishes
   - C. faucets
   - D. water or other liquid

4. a brave *constable*
   - A. explorer
   - B. law officer
   - C. pilot
   - D. social worker

5. a slide *projector*
   - A. machine for checking slides
   - B. machine for making slides
   - C. machine for showing slides
   - D. machine for selling slides

(6–10) Answer the following questions.

6. In a country where there is *communism*, you would *not* find
   - A. criminals
   - B. generals
   - C. owners of big businesses
   - D. politicians

7. What part of a new house might a *mason* build or be responsible for?
   - A. electric wiring
   - B. roof
   - C. plumbing
   - D. stone walls

8. Where might you put a *salve*?
   - A. in your mouth
   - B. on your clothes
   - C. on your face
   - D. on your shoes

9. Which of the following is an **accessory** to a murder?
   - A. a witness
   - B. someone who helps the murderer hide out
   - C. the murderer
   - D. the victim

10. Which of the following is a *verdict* in a court of law?
   - A. judge's instructions to the jury
   - B. "Not guilty"
   - C. oath of a witness
   - D. prosecutor's plea

(11–15) Fill in the missing word in the sentence.

11. Most people prefer democracy to _____.
   - A. communism
   - B. constables
   - C. fixtures
   - D. projectors

12. They spent 12 hours discussing the case, but they couldn't agree on a(n) _____.
   - A. accessory
   - B. fixture
   - C. salve
   - D. verdict

13. The _____ are skilled hunters who are even able to kill elephants with only the use of bows and arrows.
   - A. Accessories
   - B. Constables
   - C. Masons
   - D. Pygmies

14. We had a leak in the bottom of the _____, and all the dye ran out all over the terrace.
   - A. fixture
   - B. projector
   - C. salve
   - D. vat

15. That's a beautiful brick fireplace you built. I didn't know you were a(n)
_____.

    A. constable   C. projector
    B. mason   D. salve

C. Definitions for You to Derive from Context

Read the sentence following the word in bold type and on the basis of what you read, choose the correct definition.

1. **currency**
   Do you have any **currency** in your pocket? Nickels? Dimes? Dollar bills? I'll take whatever you have.

   A. comb   C. money
   B. keys   D. wallet

2. When you land at an airport in a foreign country, you find **currency** exchanges. What is a **currency** exchange?

   A. place where   C. place where you
      you buy tickets   learn the foreign
                          language
   B. place where   D. place where you
      you change   pick up your bags
      American
      money into the
      money of the
      foreign country

3. **equality**
   All we want is **equality**. We want to be treated the same as anyone else, no better and no worse.

   A. equal treatment C. lower taxes
   B. health   D. raise in pay

4. The player with the black pieces in a chess game has achieved **equality** with the white player. Who is ahead?

   A. black   C. neither player
   B. white

5. **intermission**
   There will be a 15-minute **intermission** between Act 1 and Act 2.

   A. break in the   C. new director
      action
   B. explanation of   D. program notes
      the play

6. What happens at the **intermission** of a concert performance?

   A. everyone goes   C. the curtain goes up
      home
   B. some people   D. the orchestra begins
      get up out of   playing
      their seats

7. **masterpiece**
   His second novel was his **masterpiece**, one of those rare artistic accomplishments which has truly great significance.

   A. a long book   C. a very important
      report   work of art
   B. a reward   D. something you give
                          away free

8. Which of the following is a **masterpiece**?

   A. baked beans   C. the Mississippi River
   B. Leonardo da   D. Interstate Highway 5
      Vinci's painting
      The Mona Lisa

9. **motive**

Tell me her *motive* for doing that—a reason for anyone to do that.

A. what   C. where
B. when   D. why

10. If a crime is committed without any *motive*, it is done

A. for no particular purpose   C. without any help
B. in an awkward way   D. with poor results

11. **option**

You have the *option* to choose pink or lavender.

A. beauty   C. penalty
B. choice   D. worth

12. A person who has *options* has

A. great success   C. strange thoughts
B. many relatives   D. the right to decide

13. **rehearsal**

The final *rehearsal* for the play is on Friday evening. It is our last chance to get ready for the performances scheduled for Saturday and Sunday.

A. happy ending   C. practice session
B. new version   D. unexpected result

14. Which of the following is most likely to have *rehearsals*?

A. group of musicians   C. students in a class
B. sales clerks in a store   D. waiters in a restaurant

15. **scandal**

My mother said that what we had done was a *scandal* which brought shame on the whole family.

A. disgrace   C. news
B. family reunion   D. reward

16. opposite of *scandal*

A. explanation   C. loss of appetite
B. honor   D. poverty

17. **shortage**

The *shortage* of gasoline in the 1970's meant that you had to wait in long lines at the filling stations before you could fill up your tank—and then sometimes they would only let you buy five or ten gallons.

A. fine quality   C. necessary amount
B. loss   D. not enough of something

18. opposite of *shortage*

A. above the ground   C. plenty
B. bargain   D. tall person

19. **trait**

Do you want to know some of Maria's *traits*? She gets angry easily. She will not ride in the back seat of the car. She never spends a penny on anything. She has beautiful eyes and a very athletic figure.

A. attitudes of others   C. treatment
B. special qualities   D. ways of getting to school

20. A description of your *traits* helps to explain

A. how much money you make   C. where you live
B. what kind of person you are   D. where your family came from

D. Nouns for You to Look Up in the Dictionary

(1–5) Each of the nouns in bold type has to do with religion, at least in part of its definition. Unless you are sure you know the word's meaning, look it up in the dictionary. Then choose the word or phrase with a similar meaning.

1. the **pulpit** of the church

   A. the bell tower
   B. the chapel
   C. the holy image
   D. the platform used by the preacher

2. rest on the **Sabbath**

   A. celebration of Lent
   B. floor of the church
   C. place where you kneel to pray
   D. seventh day of the week

3. the Holy **Scriptures**

   A. Apostles
   B. Christmas and Easter
   C. saints
   D. the Bible

4. a sacred **shrine**

   A. book of the Bible
   B. hymn
   C. holy object or place
   D. word of God

5. the Old **Testament**

   A. part of Jerusalem
   B. part of the Bible
   C. strong religious feeling
   D. the Catholic Church in Roman times

(6–7) Answer the following questions.

6. What is another meaning of **testament?**

   A. courage
   B. part of the body
   C. treatment
   D. will

7. What is a **pulpit** mainly used for?

   A. collecting alms
   B. holding up the church
   C. prayer
   D. preaching

(8–10) Fill in the missing word in the sentence.

8. For Jews, Saturday is the _____.

   A. Sabbath
   B. Scripture
   C. shrine
   D. Testament

9. Many _____ are containers for sacred relics.

   A. pulpits
   B. Sabbaths
   C. shrines
   D. Testaments

10. In general, the word _____ means holy writing.

   A. pulpit
   B. scripture
   C. shrine
   D. testament

E. Nouns with More than One Meaning

All of the words in this lesson are nouns which have more than one common meaning.

circuit   a. Path or route.

b. In electricity, the path of the current in an electrical device. The way the wires and other parts of the device are arranged.

faculty   a. Mental gift, special ability.

b. Teachers at a school or college.

frill   a. A fancy edging on clothing.

b. (often plural—*frills*) Anything that is too fancy, wasteful or unnecessary.

registration   a. The act of signing up (for example, for the draft).

b. A license to own a car.

c. The number of people registered, the enrollment.

renewal   a. Doing something a second time.

b. Fixing something up like new.

c. Getting an extension on such a thing as a license or a lease that is running out.

(1–3) Choose the word or phrase with the **same** meaning, or almost the same meaning, as the word in bold type.

1. school *registration*

   A. administration

   B. classes

   C. rules and regulations

   D. students enrolled

2. college *faculty*

   A. degree

   B. place to live

   C. professors

   D. reputation

3. short in the *circuit*

   A. plan

   B. radio

   C. result

   D. wiring

(4–5) Choose the word or phrase with the **opposite** meaning, or with the meaning which is most nearly opposite.

4. no-*frills* flight

   A. excitement

   B. necessities

   C. paying passengers

   D. short delays

5. in need of *renewal*

   A. a slowdown

   B. dullness

   C. getting worse

   D. poverty

(6–8) Answer the following questions.

6. Which part of your body is associated with your **faculties**?

   A. back   C. head
   B. feet   D. stomach

7. When do you get a **renewal** on a driver's license?

   A. when the old license runs out
   B. when you first learn how to drive
   C. when you get enough money together
   D. when you have had lots of accidents

8. Police Officer Kesel stopped Johnny Krueger on the highway and asked for his **registration**, meaning

   A. name and address
   B. license for the car
   C. money
   D. proof of insurance

(9–10) Fill in the missing word in the sentence.

9. My uncle is a famous writer who not only writes books, but also goes on the college lecture _____, giving talks at colleges across the country.

   A. circuit   C. renewal
   B. faculty   D. registration

10. Jane's blouse has a lovely lace _____ at the bottom.

   A. circuit   C. frill
   B. faculty   D. renewal

F. Words with the Prefix *Ex-*

The prefix **ex-** means "out of" or "out from" or "away." In some words, it has the form **e-**.

exclamation   [*noun*] A loud statement or strong protest. From **ex-** + a form of a Latin word meaning "to cry out." An **exclamation** is a sharp cry that just bursts out of a person.

exclude   [*verb*] To keep someone or something from being included. From **ex-** + a form of a Latin word meaning "to close."

expectation   [*noun*] Hope for the future, what you **expect** to happen. From **ex-** + a form of a Latin word meaning "to look at." An **expectation** results from your looking away from the present and into the future.

exquisite   [*adjective*] Very beautiful. From **ex-** + a from of a Latin word meaning "to seek." Something that is **exquisite** has been sought out and carefully selected and is therefore beautiful and fine.

extract   a. [*verb*] To take out, to pull out. From **ex-** + a form of a Latin word meaning "to pull."

         b. [*noun*] An essential part of a particular food or other product that has been separated out.

(1–3) Choose the word or phrase with the **same** meaning, or almost the same meaning, as the word in bold type.

1. **expectation** about the result
   - A. confusion
   - B. disappointment
   - C. prediction
   - D. things to be said

2. an **exclamation** of joy
   - A. cause
   - B. feeling
   - C. shout
   - D. song

3. to **exclude** everyone over 16
   - A. encourage
   - B. find fault with
   - C. keep out
   - D. point out

(4–6) Choose the word or phrase with the **opposite** meaning, or with the meaning which is most nearly opposite.

4. to **extract** the cream
   - A. enrich
   - B. leave in
   - C. put away
   - D. refuse to swallow

5. an **exquisite** dress
   - A. inexpensive
   - B. short
   - C. simple
   - D. ugly

6. **excluding** the tip
   - A. dividing up
   - B. figuring out
   - C. including
   - D. wasting

(7–8) Answer the following questions.

7. In grammar, an **exclamation** point (!) at the end of a sentence tells you the sentence is
   - A. a quote
   - B. incomplete
   - C. part of a paragraph
   - D. worth paying attention to

8. When would you be most likely to use the word **exquisite**?
   - A. to describe a bruise on your knee
   - B. to describe a garbage dump
   - C. to describe a great painting
   - D. to describe the cost of lunch

(9–10) Fill in the missing word in the sentence.

9. When you go shopping, buy some vanilla _____. It comes in a tiny glass container.
   - A. exclamation
   - B. exclusion
   - C. expectation
   - D. extract

10. What is your _____ for how well our team will do this weekend?
    - A. exclamation
    - B. exclusion
    - C. expectation
    - D. extract

G. Chapter 3 Review

(1–7) Choose the word or phrase with the **same** meaning, or almost the same meaning, as the word in bold type.

1. built by the *mason*

   A. architect   C. carpenter
   B. bricklayer   D. contractor

2. suffering from *nausea*

   A. chest pain   C. loss of blood
   B. fever   D. upset stomach

3. bought a *salve*

   A. birthday gift   C. place to store things
   B. ointment   D. stove or refrigerator

4. announce the *verdict*

   A. decision   C. starting lineup
   B. news release   D. winner of the prize

5. *extract* a tooth

   A. clean   C. make a model of
   B. kill the pain of D. pull out

6. call my *attorney*

   A. friend   C. relative
   B. lawyer   D. teacher

7. an *exquisite* picture

   A. detailed   C. upsetting
   B. gorgeous   D. very old

(8–12) Choose the word or phrase with the **opposite** meaning, or with the meaning which is most nearly opposite.

8. *equality* in pay

   A. about as ex-   C. difference
      pected
   B. a cut   D. high amount

9. headed for a *collision*

   A. avoiding each   C. loss of faith
      other
   B. friendly greeting D. rising to the top

10. a *juvenile* court

   A. for criminal   C. for marriage
      cases
   B. for important   D. for older people
      lawsuits

11. a group of *pygmies*

   A. clean beings   C. sinners
   B. intelligent ani- D. tall people
      mals

12. created a *masterpiece*

   A. amusing inci-   C. lasting result
      dent
   B. free country   D. unimportant painting

(13–17) Fill in the missing word in the sentence.

13. Sunday is the _____.

   A. pulpit   C. Scripture
   B. Sabbath   D. testament

14. They put the undershirts in big _____ filled with dye.

   A. accessories   C. projectors
   B. circuits   D. vats

15. The band had a(n) _____ last night to get ready for the concert on Sunday.

   A. expectation   C. rehearsal
   B. intermission   D. scandal

16. Have they found a(n) _____ for the crime?

   A. exclamation   C. option
   B. motive   D. trait

17. British policemen are called

_____.

A. constables   C. pedestrians
B. lecturers   D. shrines

(18–19) Choose the word that has the two meanings that are in bold type.

18. *mental gifts*; *teachers at a college*

A. aptitudes   C. professors
B. faculties   D. talents

19. *fixing something up like new*; *extension on a lease*

A. renewal   C. resigning
B. renovation   D. restoration

(20) Pick out the best sentence to go with the definition.

20. number of people registered

A. Does he have his *registration* for the draft?
B. What is the *registration* at the University of Texas?
C. Where is the car *registration*?

(21) Answer the following question.

21. What does the prefix **ex-** in **extract** mean?

A. by   C. of
B. former   D. out

(22–23) Look carefully at the pairs of words in capitals. Try to figure out the relationship between each pair. Then choose the sentence that does the **best** job of showing how the words are related.

22. ATTORNEYS : LAW

A. Attorneys have to be careful of the law.
B. Attorneys love the law.
C. Attorneys practice law.

23. DOLLAR : CURRENCY

A. The dollar can be sold for currency.
B. The dollar is a type of currency.
C. The dollar is better than currency.

(24–25) Figure out how the first two words in capitals are related to each other. Then choose the pair of words below it that are related in the same way.

24. ATTORNEYS : LAW

A. DOCTORS : MEDICINE
B. DRIVERS : ACCIDENT
C. SOLDIERS : UNIFORM

25. DOLLAR : CURRENCY

A. ROBIN : BIRD
B. ROBIN : NEST
C. ROBIN : SING

CHAPTER 4.

Words in this chapter:

adviser

boredom

calories
casserole
chowder
classification

delicatessen
dimension
discipline

economy
emigrant
emotion
exile

garlic

habitation
hostage

infinite
initiation
inspiration
installment
intersection

lotion

maintenance
maneuver
matrimony
midday
mishap

nomination

precipitation
predicament
prepaid
prescribe
prescription
preview
proclamation
prosperity

reaction
readiness
recorder
recovery
reflex
resource

scoundrel
sequence

uproar

A. Nouns with Simple Definitions

emotion	deep feeling
matrimony	marriage
midday	the middle of the day
mishap	an unfortunate occurrence, an accident
predicament	a difficult situation
proclamation	an official announcement
readiness	condition of being prepared
reflex	an automatic response
scoundrel	an evil, worthless person
uproar	loud disturbance

(1–5) Choose the word or phrase with the **same** meaning, or almost the same meaning, as the word in bold type.

1. the sun at *midday*

   A. daybreak   C. morning
   B. evening   D. noon

2. a way out of the *predicament*

   A. jam   C. prison
   B. maze   D. tunnel

3. heard of your *mishap*

   A. award   C. sickness
   B. misfortune   D. strange story

4. caused an *uproar*

   A. awakening   C. disorder
   B. break   D. sadness

5. keep that *scoundrel* away

   A. bad odor   C. vicious animal
   B. dangerous con- D. villain
      dition

(6–10) Answer the following questions.

6. What ceremony leads to *matrimony*?

   A. birthday   C. graduation
   B. confirmation D. wedding

7. Who has to have good *reflexes*?

   A. actor   C. musician
   B. boxer   D. writer

8. Who sometimes makes *proclamations*?

   A. a member of C. the family doctor
      the jury
   B. a policeman   D. the governor

9. Which is a sign of *emotion*?

   A. a haircut   C. sunny skies
   B. bleeding from a D. tears or laughter
      cut

10. Which of the following words is related to the word *readiness*?

   A. re   C. ready
   B. read   D. red

(11–15) Fill in the missing word in the sentence.

11. I wouldn't want to get stuck in a(n)
    _____ like that.
    A. emotion   C. proclamation
    B. predicament   D. scoundrel

12. President Lincoln issued a(n)
    _____ freeing the slaves.
    A. mishap   C. proclamation
    B. predicament   D. uproar

13. The doctor tapped on my knee to test my
    _____.
    A. emotion   C. readiness
    B. matrimony   D. reflex

14. Just the sight of her causes me to feel the
    strangest _____.
    A. emotion   C. readiness
    B. matrimony   D. reflex

15. That _____ stole every cent I
    had.
    A. midday   C. proclamation
    B. mishap   D. scoundrel

B. Nouns with Longer Definitions

dimension	Size in one direction, such as the length, the width, or the height. Or, more generally, the extent of something, such as the "*dimension*" of a problem.
emigrant	A person who leaves his or her country to settle in another.
exile	A person who has been forced to leave his or her country and live elsewhere. Also, we speak of people living *in exile*, the condition of being forced to live outside your own country. As a *verb*, *to exile* means to force a person to leave his or her own country.
hostage	A person seized and held captive until demands made by the captors are met. *Hostages* are sometimes taken in warfare, or in acts of terrorism, or by criminals who are cornered.
infinite	Going on forever, without end. Bigger or more extensive than you can measure or even imagine. *Infinite* can also be used as an *adjective* meaning going on forever.
maintenance	Keeping things in order. In particular, keeping a building in shape or keeping machines in good working order.
maneuver	The move or series of moves made to gain an advantage, as in war, a fight, a game, business, etc. Also, (*verb*) to make such a move or series of moves.
nomination	The process of naming someone as a candidate for political office. Or, in general, naming someone for any purpose.
prosperity	Being well off economically. Or a period of time when the economy is doing well.

43

resource   Something you can fall back on. Or a source of supply. In particular, (usually plural) the basic sources of the economy of a region, such as land or minerals, etc.

(1–4) Choose the word or phrase with the **same** meaning, or almost the same meaning, as the word in bold type.

1. an *infinite* series

   A. additional   C. fascinating
   B. endless   D. reversed

2. find its *dimensions*

   A. measurements   C. unusual qualities
   B. secrets   D. weaknesses

3. country with a lot of *resources*

   A. basic wealth   C. friends
   B. different types   D. problems
      of people

4. *nomination* for governor

   A. candidacy   C. election
   B. defeat   D. term of office

(5–7) Choose the word or phrase with the **opposite** meaning, or with the meaning which is most nearly opposite.

5. a group of *exiles*

   A. complainers   C. former employees
   B. givers   D. people welcomed
                back

6. a period of *prosperity*

   A. bad times   C. lack of opportunity
   B. freedom   D. warfare

7. *maintenance* on the car

   A. failure to make C. interior
     repairs
   B. high mileage   D. low value

(8–10) Answer the following questions.

8. The policeman surprised the robber while he was holding up the bank. The bank manager escaped, but the robber seized one of the customers whom he said he would not release unless he could talk to the newspapers.

   Who is the *hostage* in this story?

   A. bank manager C. policeman
   B. customer   D. robber

9. What do *emigrants* and *exiles* have in common

   A. both have   C. both like to stay put
     broken the law
   B. both have left   D. both work for the
     their own coun-   government
     tries

10. Where would you be most likely to find a *maneuver*?

   A. bag of nails   C. chocolate cake
   B. chess game   D. clothing store

(11–15) Fill in the missing word in the sentence.

11. My Uncle Steven thinks of himself as living in _____ , but it was his choice to leave home and move to Paris.

    A. dimension   C. the infinite
    B. exile   D. prosperity

12. Marcia has refused the _____ for class president.

    A. maintenance   C. nomination
    B. maneuver   D. resource

13. The terrorists have taken over the plane and are holding 47 passengers as _____ .

    A. emigrants   C. hostages
    B. exiles   D. resources

14. We have a contract with a company to do the _____ on all of our computers.

    A. dimensions   C. maneuvers
    B. maintenance   D. nominations

15. The _____ is something that goes on and on and on.

    A. dimension   C. prosperity
    B. infinite   D. resource

C. Definitions for You to Derive from Context

Read the sentence following the word in bold type and on the basis of what you read, choose the correct definition.

1. **adviser**

   The high school has **advisers** to help students handle personal problems and to help them with their thinking about what courses to take, what careers they might want to follow, what they're going to do after high school, and so on. (Also spelled **advisor**.)

   A. people who cause problems
   B. people who give advice
   C. people who run businesses
   D. people who teach English

2. The suffix **-er** as in **adviser**, employ**er**, and teach**er** means

   A. condition of   C. person who
   B. not   D. the most

3. **boredom**

   Aunt Lilly and Uncle Harry are so dull. Whenever we visit them, I feel such **boredom** I almost go to sleep.

   A. desire   C. feeling of being bored
   B. expectation   D. love

4. opposite of **boredom**

   A. excitement   C. greed
   B. loss of energy D. strength

5. **classification**

   I used a system of **classification**, putting all of them into groups which I labeled A,B,C,D,E, and F.

   A. final notice   C. organization into categories
   B. homeroom class D. the first letters of the alphabet

45

6. Where would you be most likely to find *classifications*?

   A. in the grass on your front lawn
   B. in a painting
   C. in a science book
   D. on your big toe

7. **habitation**

   There is no doubt people were living here. We have found all sorts of evidence of *habitation*.

   A. a battle
   B. a forest
   C. a habit
   D. a settlement

8. *Habitation* can also refer to just a single

   A. gym
   B. machine
   C. place to live
   D. theater

9. **intersection**

   You'll come to an *intersection* where Maple Street crosses Lincoln Avenue.

   A. finish line
   B. highway
   C. movement up and down
   D. place where two things meet

10. What best describes an *intersection*?

    A. circle
    B. cross
    C. square
    D. very long line

11. **lotion**

    Most of those things you rub on your skin to make it soft or to take care of pimples and that type of thing come in the form of either creams or *lotions*. I prefer *lotions* because all you have to do is pour them on.

    A. device for strengthening muscles
    B. food
    C. liquid you put on your skin
    D. pill

12. Some of the *lotions* you buy are intended for use

    A. for an upset stomach
    B. in your eyes
    C. on your face and hands
    D. to protect your heart

13. **reaction**

    When Natalie told Joe she loves him, you should have seen his *reaction*! You never would have guessed the way he responded.

    A. fear
    B. position in life
    C. response
    D. way of dressing

14. The word *reaction* is related to the word

    A. ace
    B. action
    C. read
    D. real

15. **recorder**

    You need a tape *recorder* to make copies of those songs.

    A. measuring device
    B. person or device that records
    C. singer
    D. songwriter

16. John Alroy uses a *recorder* to help him in his college classes.

    A. answers exam questions
    B. gets him to class on time
    C. takes down what the teacher says
    D. writes his papers

17. **recovery**

    What an amazing *recovery*! Everyone expected her to die, and here she is healthy again.

    A. answer
    B. beginning
    C. getting well again
    D. paying your bills

18. Which of the folowing describes a *recovery*?

    A. a dancer gets up gracefully after falling down
    B. a man buys six pairs of sneakers at the shoe store
    C. an actor makes a long speech
    D. a newly married couple buys a house

19. **sequence**

    Here is the *sequence* from beginning to end, with all of the steps in order.

    A. accomplishment
    B. decoration
    C. event
    D. series

20. If you describe a **sequence**, you describe

    A. how big some-   C. how it looks
       thing is

    B. how it goes   D. how much you like it
       from one point to
       another

D. Nouns for You to Look Up in the Dictionary

(1–5) Each of the nouns in bold type has to do with food, at least in part of its definition. Unless you are sure you know the word's meaning, look it up. Then choose the word or phrase with a similar meaning.

1. too many **calories**

    A. ingredients   C. spices
    B. sauces   D. units for measuring
                     the energy in food

2. baked in a **casserole**

    A. deep dish   C. muffin tin
    B. metal pan   D. oven

3. clam **chowder**

    A. fried dish   C. served raw
    B. recipe   D. soup

4. buy it at the **delicatessen**

    A. bakery   C. supermarket
    B. store special- D. vegetable stand
       izing in cooked
       cold meats

5. cooked with **garlic**

    A. green vegetable C. strong-smelling
                         seasoning
    B. meat juice   D. type of cooking oil

(6–8) Answer the following questions.

6. What color is raw **garlic**?

    A. green   C. white
    B. red

7. Why do people worry about **calories**?

    A. calories take too C. people are afraid of
       long to cook   getting fat
    B. calories can
       make food taste
       bad

8. **Casserole** dishes are

    A. baked   C. fried
    B. boiled

(9–10) Fill in the missing word in the sentence.

9. Most _____ are thick soups that contain fish or shellfish, or sometimes vegetables.

    A. calories   C. chowders
    B. casseroles   D. garlics

10. Mother bought some shrimp salad at the _____ counter.

    A. casserole   C. delicatessen
    B. chowder   D. garlic

E. Nouns with More than One Meaning

All of the words in this lesson are nouns which have more than one common meaning. The first word (*discipline*) can also have additional meanings as a verb.

discipline   a. A field of study.

b. Great self-control.

c. Punishment.

d. A set of strict rules.

e. [*verb*] To punish.

f. [*verb*] To train a person or group, such as a class or a military unit, by making sure they obey the rules and are orderly.

economy   a. Thriftiness.

b. A country's system of doing business, the way its economic life is run.

initiation   a. The act of starting something.

b. The special ceremony that takes place when a person joins certain types of organizations, such as college clubs and fraternities.

inspiration   a. The act of inhaling air.

b. A very strong influence, someone or something you admire very much.

c. A sudden clever thought.

installment (or
instalment)   a. One of the payments on a loan that is paid back in stages.

b. A part in a series, particularly a part in a continuing story broken into a series of parts.

(1–5) Choose the word or phrase with the **opposite** meaning, or with the meaning which is most nearly opposite.

1. *in installments*

   A. all together   C. heavy items
   B. fast movement   D. repaired

2. *initiation* of a project

   A. bad results   C. support
   B. major part   D. winding up

3. *economy* of means

   A. abundance   C. poor person
   B. not a matter   D. wastefulness

4. *discipline* the students

   A. learn from   C. take notice of
   B. reward   D. walk away from

5. a sign of *inspiration*

   A. breathing out   C. growth
   B. failure   D. weariness

(6–7) Answer the following questions.

6. The word *initiation* refers to
   - A. the beginning of something
   - B. the end of something
   - C. the middle of something
   - D. the time when two events happen together

7. What does it mean to have an *installment* loan?
   - A. you make regular payments
   - B. you pay it all back at the end of a certain period
   - C. you pay a small amount now, the rest later
   - D. you pay upon demand

(8–9) Fill in the missing word in the sentence.

8. The newspapers predict the
   _____ will grow at a strong rate for the rest of this year.
   - A. discipline
   - B. economy
   - C. inspiration
   - D. installment

9. Mrs. Jones' struggle to save her farm has been a(n) _____ to all of us.
   - A. discipline
   - B. initiation
   - C. inspiration
   - D. installment

(10) Pick out the best sentence to go with the definition.

10. a field of study
    - A. The Marine Corps has strict *discipline*.
    - B. You have to have strong *discipline* to play chess well.
    - C. Biology is one of the scientific *disciplines*.

F. Words with the Prefix *Pre-*

Pre- usually means "before," as in *prefix*. Sometimes it also means "extremely."

precipitation [*noun*] Rainfall or snowfall. Also, the result of an action, particularly a sudden action. From a Latin word meaning "to throw down headlong." In the word *precipitation*, the *pre-* means "extremely," not "before."

prepaid [*adjective*] Paid in advance. (Surprisingly, *prepaid* means the same as *postpaid*.)

prescribe [*verb*] To set forth a rule or directions. In particular, to write up a *prescription* (see below) for drugs or medicine. *Prescribe* comes from *pre-* + a form of a Latin word meaning "to write." When you *prescribe*, you write down your message right at the beginning, where it can be seen.

prescription [*noun*] The note a doctor writes to allow you to buy a particular medicine. Or the medicine itself. Or more generally, a set of directions or rules for obtaining a particular goal. *Prescription* comes from *prescribe* (above).

preview [*verb*] To see in advance. From *pre-* + *view*. Also [*noun*] an advance showing, a hint at what is to come.

(1–3) Choose the word or phrase with the **same** meaning, or almost the same meaning, as the word in bold type.

1. heavy **precipitation**

   A. debts   C. smog
   B. rain   D. weight

2. **prescription** for success

   A. desire   C. rewards
   B. detailed plan   D. striving

3. to **preview the movie**

   A. buy a ticket for   C. walk out on it
   it
   B. see it before it   D. write a review
   is shown   about it
   generally

(4–6) Choose the word or phrase with the **opposite** meaning, or with the meaning which is most nearly opposite.

4. **prepaid** charges

   A. below cost   C. paid after you got
                      the goods
   B. following   D. unreasonable

5. chances of **precipitation**

   A. dryness   C. living
   B. flight   D. losing

6. a sneak **preview**

   A. something barely C. something you saw
   seen   twice
   B. something seen   D. something you saw
   after everyone   when no one was
   else saw it   looking

(7–10) Answer the following questions.

7. What kinds of drugs are **prescription** drugs?

   A. drugs only a   C. drugs you pay for in
   doctor can   advance
   prescribe
   B. drugs that are   D. drugs you take in
   harmless but   advance
   often helpful

8. What do you think of when you think of **precipitation**?

   A. basketball   C. getting wet
   B. eggs   D. good grades

9. The root words in **prescribe** and **prescription** have to do with

   A. fame   C. sunshine
   B. running   D. writing

10. Many companies that sell by mail order ask that their charges be **prepaid**. What does this mean?

   A. the amount you   C. you pay when the
   pay is figured   goods are delivered
   out by a com-
   puter
   B. you send in   D. you wait for the
   your money,   company to bill you
   then
   get what you
   ordered

G. Chapter 4 Review

(1–7) Choose the word or phrase with the **same** meaning, or almost the same meaning, as the word in bold type.

1. living *in exile*

   A. imprisoned
   B. in luxury
   C. outside your own country
   D. to old age

2. take *hostages*

   A. beatings
   B. captives
   C. chances
   D. liberties

3. shipping *prepaid*

   A. by truck
   B. insured
   C. paid in advance
   D. rapidly

4. test your *reflexes*

   A. automatic responses
   B. general health
   C. mental condition
   D. strength

5. upset his *emotions*

   A. abilities
   B. actions
   C. feelings
   D. sense of balance

6. *maintenance* on the bridge

   A. balance
   B. cables
   C. repairs
   D. tolls

7. the subject of *matrimony*

   A. adulthood
   B. first names
   C. marriage
   D. motherhood

(8–12) Choose the word or phrase with the **opposite** meaning, or with the meaning which is most nearly opposite.

8. the *emigrants* at the dock

   A. former sailors
   B. officials
   C. passengers boarding the ship
   D. people who stay home

9. the *midday* sun

   A. blazing
   B. early
   C. midnight
   D. winter

10. an *infinite* amount

    A. heavy
    B. limited
    C. temporary
    D. uncounted

11. *readiness* to take action

    A. discouraging advice
    B. lack of preparation
    C. planning
    D. strong desire

12. the *recovery* of the jewels

    A. hiding
    B. inside
    C. loss
    D. purchase

(13–17) Fill in the missing word in the sentence.

13. Add a touch of _____ and a half teaspoon of salt.

    A. calories
    B. casserole
    C. chowder
    D. garlic

14. Snow is a form of _____.

    A. delicatessen
    B. habitation
    C. precipitation
    D. uproar

15. It's at the _____ of Collins Avenue and 163rd Street.

    A. classification
    B. dimension
    C. intersection
    D. proclamation

16. We'll take item number 14 out of _____.

    A. boredom
    B. prescription
    C. reaction
    D. sequence

17. Mom paid the final _____ on the car loan this month.

    A. installment   C. preview
    B. mishap   D. resource

(18–19) Choose the word that has the two meanings that are in bold type.

18. *thriftiness*; *economic system*

    A. economy   C. frugality
    B. employment   D. enterprise

19. *breathing in*; *strong influence*

    A. authority   C. inspiration
    B. inhaling   D. prestige

(20) Pick out the best sentence to go with the definition.

20. great self-control

    A. Calculus is one of the math *disciplines*.
    B. One of the things you need to become a good tennis player is *discipline*.
    C. The *discipline* in the Marine Corps is tough.

(21) Answer the following question.

21. What does the prefix *pre-* in *prescribe* mean?

    A. against   C. extremely
    B. before   D. for

(22–23) Look carefully at the pairs of words in capitals. Try to figure out the relationship between each pair. Then choose the sentence that does the **best** job of showing how the words are related.

22. SCOUNDREL : BAD

    A. A scoundrel has a bad life.
    B. A scoundrel is a bad person.
    C. A scoundrel lives in bad surroundings.

23. STREETS : INTERSECTION

    A. Streets are more useful than an intersection.
    B. Streets cross at an intersection.
    C. Streets end at an intersection.

(24–25) Figure out how the first two words in capitals are related to each other. Then choose the pair of words below it that are related in the same way.

24. SCOUNDREL : BAD

    A. SAINT : GOOD
    B. TEACHER : LEARN
    C. THIEF : RICH

25. STREETS : INTERSECTION

    A. RAILS : TRAIN
    B. ROPES : TANGLE
    C. PIPES : JOINT

CHAPTER 5.

Words in this chapter:

accommodate

brows
browse

capsize
clarify
cleanse

depress
disinherit
dislocate
dislodge
dispense

evacuate
exceed

fidget
flinch
foretell

inhale
integrate
intoxicate
invest

jilt

lessen
lesson

mingle
misjudge
mislead
misplace
mobilize
modify
mutilate

nominate

omit
overhaul
overlap

penalize
perforate
poach

resume

singe
strive
suffocate
suite
sweet
swivel

tracked
tract
trance
trans-

violation

yearn

A. Verbs with Simple Definitions

clarify	to make clear or understandable
cleanse	to make clean
exceed	to go beyond a limit, to perform better
foretell	to predict
inhale	to breathe in, to take into your lungs
intoxicate	to make drunk
jilt	to cast aside a lover
omit	to leave out
strive	to work hard to obtain
yearn	to have a deep desire for something

(1–5) Choose the word or phrase with the **same** meaning, or almost the same meaning, as the word in bold type.

1. **yearning** for peace

   A. effort
   B. longing
   C. movement
   D. reward

2. to **strive** for success

   A. desire
   B. prepare
   C. single out
   D. struggle

3. to **exceed** the goals

   A. change
   B. make up
   C. outdo
   D. see

4. a **jilted** girlfriend

   A. abandoned
   B. attractive
   C. newly acquired
   D. spoiled

5. able to **foretell**

   A. live happily
   B. make a living
   C. perform magic
   D. see the future

(6–10) Choose the word or phrase with the **opposite** meaning, or with the meaning which is most nearly opposite.

6. to **inhale** freely

   A. die
   B. force air out
   C. receive advice
   D. save money

7. to **omit** important facts

   A. correctly identify
   B. forget about
   C. include
   D. list in the opposite order

8. to go home **intoxicated**

   A. early
   B. healthy
   C. less well informed
   D. sober

9. to **cleanse** her record

   A. dirty
   B. leave unchanged
   C. not care about
   D. subtract from

10. to *clarify* an important matter
  A. confuse
  B. correct
  C. fail to succeed at
  D. tell someone about

(11–15) Fill in the missing word in the sentence.

11. Smokers who _____ do even worse damage to their health.
  A. cleanse
  B. exceed
  C. inhale
  D. intoxicate

12. Rebecca spent six weeks working on the school play, but her name was _____ from the list of credits.
  A. clarified
  B. foretold
  C. jilted
  D. omitted

13. The number of people who signed up for the bike tour far _____ the number Mr. Samuels was expecting.
  A. clarifies
  B. exceeds
  C. foretells
  D. strives

14. You _____ for success, but you don't do any work to obtain it.
  A. exceed
  B. intoxicate
  C. strive
  D. yearn

15. Your letter of April 6 has been most helpful to me, but I'm not sure I understand the last paragraph. Could you _____ it for me?
  A. clarify
  B. cleanse
  C. foretell
  D. strive

B. Verbs with Longer Definitions

disinherit	To disown, particularly to disown one of your children and to keep him or her from inheriting any of your belongings or money.
dislocate	To disrupt, to move something out of place. In particular, to disconnect two bones that are supposed to connect to each other.
evacuate	To withdraw people or things from a dangerous situation, to empty out.
flinch	To show fear, to shrink back in fear. In particular, to do such things as blink or tense your muscles as an automatic response to a threat.
integrate	To unify, to put together, to bring something into a larger unit. In particular, to make such things as schools *integrated*, that is, open to everyone, no matter what their race or religion.
mobilize	To get ready for action. In particular, to call up troops and get ready for war.
mutilate	To cripple, to cut up; for example, to cut off a limb of the body.
singe	To burn lightly, to put quickly through a flame, as for example, when you burn off hair.
suffocate	To cut off the supply of air. Or to die from lack of air.

swivel   To spin around or turn to one side, as for example, when you turn around in the type of chair that allows you to swing from side to side.

(1–5) Choose the word or phrase with the **same** meaning, or almost the same meaning, as the word in bold type.

1. to **mutilate** in combat

   A. defeat   C. fail
   B. disable   D. show great courage

2. a seat that **swivels**

   A. has a soft seat   C. rocks back
   B. is fitted to your D. twists
      shape

3. to **evacuate** all the children

   A. give baths to   C. remove
   B. register   D. talk to

4. an **integrated** group of businesses

   A. formed into a C. specialized
      whole
   B. recently started D. well-managed

5. to **singe** a chicken

   A. chop up   C. raise
   B. put through D. take the
      a fire   skin off

(6–10) Choose the word or phrase with the **opposite** meaning, or with the meaning which is most nearly opposite.

6. to **mobilize** the army

   A. break up   C. give orders to
   B. criticize   D. move toward the
                battle

7. to **disinherit** your relatives

   A. go to see   C. put in your will
   B. keep track of D. show respect for

8. trying to **suffocate**

   A. experience pain C. remember the past
   B. feed oxygen to D. silence

9. will make you **flinch**

   A. become hopeful C. succeed
      about the future
   B. jump up   D. take on without fear

10. plans have been **dislocated**

    A. made clearer   C. seen by an outside
                   person
    B. moved forward D. straightened out

(11–12) Answer the following questions.

11. The prefix **dis-** in **disinherit** means

    A. add to   C. exactly
    B. do the opposite D. try
       of

12. What part of your body are you most likely to **dislocate**?

    A. eyes   C. heart
    B. hair   D. shoulder

(13–15) Fill in the missing word in the sentence.

13. The exit to the fire escape was locked and as a result, 12 people _____ to death in the fire.

    A. dislocated   C. singed
    B. evacuated   D. suffocated

14. Look me straight in the eye and when I make a sudden movement, try not to _____.

    A. flinch   C. mutilate
    B. mobilize   D. swivel

15. A(n) _____ circuit is one where several electronic parts are all included on one tiny chip.

   A. evacuated   C. mobilized
   B. integrated   D. swiveled

C. Definitions for You to Derive from Context

Read the sentence following the word in bold type and on the basis of what you read, choose the correct definition.

1. **capsize**
   If the wind is too strong, it can *capsize* a sailboat. And when that happens, it is awfully hard to turn the boat right-side-up again.

   A. blow a hole in   C. turn over
   B. tear the sails off of   D. weaken

2. Where do things *capsize*?

   A. in the home   C. in the streets
   B. in the ocean   D. under the earth

3. **dislodge**
   They attacked with a huge army, but we were dug in deep and they were unable to *dislodge* us from our position.

   A. assault   C. force away
   B. carry   D. see

4. opposite of *dislodge*

   A. leave in place   C. retire
   B. recover   D. tear down

5. **fidget**
   Stop *fidgeting* with the change in your pocket. There is no reason to be nervous just because you're two hours late for school.

   A. being late   C. moving around nervously
   B. counting   D. paying

6. When are people *fidgety*?

   A. when they are born   C. when they are running a race
   B. when they are restless   D. when they are sleeping

7. **invest**
   I plan to *invest* several hundred dollars in the new company because I think I will eventually make a lot of money from the deal.

   A. lay out money with the hope of profit   C. run a business
   B. pay taxes   D. start up a new company

8. Among the things people are most likely to *invest* in are

   A. hospital bills   C. stocks and bonds
   B. rent payments   D. tolls on a highway

9. **mingle**
   We stayed by ourselves up on the hill, but John *mingled* with the crowd down on the beach.

   A. came to attention   C. mixed in
   B. fled   D. studied

10. opposite of *mingle*

   A. fluff up   C. separate out
   B. grieve   D. talk clearly

11. **nominate**

I *nominate* Karen Anne Kawa for Class Treasurer. I hope your will all vote for her.

A. make a political speech C. organize the government

B. name someone as a candidate for office D. vote

12. The word *nominate* suggests

A. elections C. medicine
B. games D. travel

13. **penalize**

The referee *penalized* us five yards for being off side.

A. announced C. punished
B. played D. sought

14. Which of the following is a *penalty*?

A. $4 to see the hockey game C. 20-day vacation

B. 10 years for armed robbery D. 20,000 feet above the ground

15. **perforate**

Manufacturers sometimes *perforate* paper so you can tear it easily along the line of *perforation*.

A. burn C. put a line of holes in
B. chop D. strengthen

16. What might you use to *perforate* something?

A. axe C. hole puncher
B. grinder D. lawn mower

17. **resume**

They had us slow down at the bend. Then they told us we could *resume* our normal speed.

A. be careful C. step on the brake
B. go back to D. turn left or right

18. opposite of *resume*

A. assist C. stop
B. refuse to pay attention to D. walk

19. **violation**

Crossing the street when the light is red is a *violation*. So is driving beyond the speed limit. So is littering paper on the street.

A. attempt C. favor
B. breaking a rule D. trick

20. What does the word *violate* suggest?

A. the law C. summer heat
B. submarines D. wisdom

D. Words Which Are Homophones

Homophones are words which sound alike but have different spellings and different meanings.

browse/brows

browse   a. [*verb*] To look over things at a slow pace, particularly to look over books in a library or a bookstore.

b. [*verb*] To feed on leaves and grass, as horses and cows do.

brows   [*noun, plural*] Eyebrows.

lessen/lesson

lessen   [*verb*] To reduce, to make smaller or less important.

lesson   [*noun*] Something to be learned, as in a school *lesson*.

suite/sweet

suite
    a. [*noun*] A group of rooms, an apartment.

    b. [*noun*] A set of furniture.

    c. [*noun*] A musical composition which puts together a series of different musical pieces.

sweet
    [*adjective*] Pleasant tasting, tasting like sugar.

tract/tracked

tract
    a. [*noun*] An area of land.

    b. [*noun*] A group of parts of the body, such as the **digestive tract**.

    c. [*noun*] A political or religious pamphlet.

tracked
    [*verb*] Followed the tracks of, trailed, as in hunting.

trance/trans-

trance
    a. [*noun*] A condition where you are awake but in a daze.

    b. [*noun*] In general, a state of mind where your thoughts wander and you are unable to act effectively.

trans-
    A prefix meaning "across."

(1–3) Choose the word or phrase with the **same** meaning, or almost the same meaning, as the word in bold type.

1. comfortable **suite** of rooms

    A. design   C. set

    B. kind   D. price

2. watch the horses **browse**

    A. graze   C. play

    B. jump   D. run

3. a large **tract**

    A. growth   C. purpose

    B. number of   D. territory
       people

(4–5) Choose the word or phrase with the **opposite** meaning, or with the meaning which is most nearly opposite.

4. put into a **trance**

    A. chains   C. difficult situation

    B. debt   D. feeling of alertness

5. hope to **lessen** the damage

    A. avoid   C. pay for

    B. increase   D. remember

(6–8) Choose the word which the phrase suggests.

6. following the bear's footprints

    A. tracked

    B. tract

7. walking in your sleep

    A. trance

    B. trans-

8. above your eyes

    A. brows

    B. browse

(9–10) Fill in the missing word in the sentence.

9. Andrew spent two hours in the library _____ over books about computer games.

   A. browsing   C. tracking
   B. lessening   D. transiting

10. Now we are going to play Tchaikowsky's "Nutcracker _____."

    A. Lesson   C. Tract
    B. Suite   D. Trans

E. Verbs with More than One Meaning

All of the words in this lesson are verbs with more than one common meaning.

accommodate   a. To adjust to a person or a situation.

                     b. To assist, to make room for, to make something available.

depress   a. To press down.

                     b. To make weaker.

                     c. To sadden.

dispense   a. To do without.

                     b. To give out in portions. In particular, to distribute medicine or pills.

modify   a. To make a change in something.

                     b. To make less extreme.

                     c. In grammar, to describe or qualify the meaning of a word: adjectives are said to *modify* nouns and adverbs to *modify* verbs.

poach   a. To cook in a liquid (as when you *poach* eggs).

                     b. To hunt or fish on someone else's property without permission.

(1–3) Choose the word or phrase with the **same** meaning, or almost the same meaning, as the word in bold type.

1. *poach* on his property

   A. dig a hole   C. erect a fence
   B. encounter   D. steal an animal

2. *accommodate to* the surroundings

   A. adapt to   C. view
   B. rearrange   D. withdraw from

3. *dispense* stomach pills

   A. administer   C. sell
   B. manufacture   D. take

(4–6) Choose the word or phrase with the **opposite** meaning, or with the meaning which is most nearly opposite.

4. **modify** her demands

   A. increase
   B. keep to herself
   C. shout
   D. stop making

5. news that **depresses me**

   A. confuses me
   B. helps me
   C. keeps me in the dark
   D. makes me happy

6. **dispense with** the extra dictionary

   A. close
   B. keep
   C. look at
   D. sell

(7–8) Pick out the best sentence to go with the definition.

7. qualify the meaning of a word

   A. Harold's Plymouth has been **modified** to give it extra speed for racing.
   B. The original version of the letter was insulting, but its tone has been **modified**.
   C. You really don't need a whole string of adjectives to **modify** that noun.

8. to press down

   A. Cynthia seems to have **depressed** her level of activity.
   B. **Depress** the lever.
   C. Funerals **depress** me.

(9–10) Fill in the missing word in the sentence.

9. How do you want them, fried, scrambled, or _____?

   A. depressed
   B. dispensed
   C. modified
   D. poached

10. On our trip out West, we found that the people everywhere went out of their way to _____ us.

   A. accommodate
   B. depress
   C. dispense
   D. modify

F. Verbs with the Prefixes *Mis-* and *Over-*

Mis- is a prefix with the meaning "bad" or "incorrect." It is a prefix that has been a part of the English language from the beginning. (It does **not** come from Latin, like most of the other prefixes in this book.)

misjudge   To make a wrong guess or a wrong judgment.

mislead   To deceive, to lead in the wrong direction.

misplace   To lose something, to put it in a place which you don't remember.

The prefix *over-* sometimes has the ordinary meaning of the word "over." At other times, it combines this meaning with a second meaning: to do something in huge amounts ("over" amounts).

overhaul   To do a complete job of repairing. *Overhaul* literally means "to drag over something," that is, to look it over carefully and repair it.

overlap   To extend over, to "lap" over, to cover a part of something else.

(1–4) Choose the word or phrase with the **same** meaning, or almost the same meaning, as the word in bold type.

1. don't want to *mislead* you

   A. cooperate with C. harm
   B. deceive   D. hold back

2. our personalities *overlap*

   A. are easy to   C. clash
      understand
   B. are fully   D. have things in
      developed   common

3. to *misjudge* the crowd's reaction

   A. anticipate   C. make a mistake
                       about
   B. encourage   D. measure

4. completely *overhauled*

   A. aware   C. missed
   B. fixed   D. moved

(5–8) Choose the word or phrase with the **opposite** meaning, or with the meaning which is most nearly opposite.

5. to *misplace* your gloves

   A. buy   C. fix
   B. find   D. return

6. to *overhaul* the truck

   A. close up   C. empty out
   B. destroy   D. race

7. a *misleading* remark

   A. accurate   C. loudly spoken
   B. corny   D. subtle

8. to *misjudge* the distance

   A. cover   C. lengthen
   B. figure out D. retreat from

(9–10) Fill in the missing word in the sentence.

9. Try to join the two pieces together so that they fit exactly, side by side, without any

   _____.

   A. misjudging   C. misplacing
   B. misleading   D. overlapping

10. My uncle always _____ his glasses and then says someone took them.

    A. misjudges   C. misplaces
    B. misleads   D. overhauls

G. Chapter 5 Review

(1–7) Choose the word or phrase with the **same** meaning, or almost the same meaning, as the word in bold type.

1. *lessen* the harm

   A. cause   C. reduce
   B. complain about   D. suffer from

2. walking in a *trance*

   A. city   C. hurry
   B. daze   D. park

3. in danger of *suffocating*

   A. being unable to C. getting old
      breathe
   B. boredom   D. losing all of your
                          possessions

4. *mobilize* the troops

   A. address   C. lead into battle
   B. call up   D. supply

5. to *cleanse* the surroundings
    A. add to   C. clean up
    B. alter   D. investigate

6. a *disinherited* son
    A. disowned   C. grown
    B. first   D. ungrateful

7. see if you *flinch*
    A. fail   C. understand
    B. show fear   D. work out your problems

(8–12) Choose the word or phrase with the **opposite** meaning, or with the meaning which is most nearly opposite.

8. heavily *penalized*
    A. disarmed   C. rewarded
    B. expected to   D. without money
       lose

9. *exceed* the plan
    A. agree to   C. dislike
    B. destroy   D. do worse than

10. *striving* for perfection
    A. not caring   C. not trying
    B. not demanding   D. not understanding

11. an *integrated* plan
    A. finished   C. poorly thought out
    B. not unified   D. unnecessary

12. *capsized* boat
    A. expensive   C. turned right side up
    B. legal   D. very large

(13–17) Fill in the missing word in the sentence.

13. Mom bought a full _____ of diningroom furniture for the new house.
    A. browse   C. suite
    B. brows   D. tract

14. Be careful carrying that candle. You could _____ your hair.
    A. overhaul   C. singe
    B. poach   D. yearn

15. Tear along the _____ line.
    A. dislodged   C. mutilated
    B. evacuated   D. perforated

16. Who knows what will happen? I cannot _____ the future.
    A. accommodate C. dispense
    B. dislocate   D. foretell

17. Do not drive while _____.
    A. clarified   C. intoxicated
    B. inhaling   D. jilted

(18–19) Choose the word that has the two meanings that are in bold type.

18. *cook in a liquid*; *hunt on someone else's property*
    A. boil   C. simmer
    B. poach   D. trespass

19. *do without*; *give out in portions*
    A. exempt   C. dispense
    B. forego   D. distribute

(20) Pick out the best sentence to go with the definition.

20. qualify the meaning of
    A. Adverbs *modify* verbs.
    B. Jane drives a *modified* Ford Thunderbird.
    C. The union was forced to *modify* its demands.

(21) Answer the following question.

21. What does the prefix *mis-* in *misjudge* mean?

    A. certainly   C. greatly
    B. exactly   D. incorrectly

(22) Look carefully at the pair of words in capitals. Try to figure out the relationship between them. Then choose the sentence that does the **best** job of showing how the words are related.

22. BROWS : EYES

    A. The brows and the eyes are both on the face.
    B. The brows are above the eyes.
    C. The brows make the eyes look better.

(23–25) Figure out how the first two words in capitals are related to each other. Then choose the pair of words below it that are related in the same way.

23. BROWS : EYES

    A. LEGS : ARMS
    B. BRAINS : EARS
    C. HAIR : HEAD

24. LESSEN : INCREASE

    A. CRAZY : MAD
    B. POOR : RICH
    C. WIN : LAUGH

25. SOAP : CLEANSE

    A. MEDICINE : CURE
    B. MEDICINE : DOCTOR
    C. MEDICINE : HOSPITAL

CHAPTER 6.

Words in this chapter:

ban
barricade
brawl
brigade

cavalry
chaplain
civilian
clamor
coincidence
collide
confederate
confidential
consequence
consequently
convict
corporation

deformity
dictator
duplicate

eclipse
embrace

fore
furlough

hazard

identity
imprint
inability

locality
lyrics

memorandum
multiple

outskirts

probability

quake

reduction
reliance
removal
requirement

specification
sponsor
static
summary
survivor

variation
veto

A. Nouns with Simple Definitions

deformity	an imperfect body condition
hazard	a danger, an obstacle
inability	being unable
locality	a particular place
lyrics	(plural) the words of a song
memorandum	a short written report
outskirts	(plural) the areas just outside a city
reliance	depending on help from someone or something
removal	taking away something, or getting rid of it
requirement	something needed for a particular purpose

(1–5) Choose the word or phrase with the **same** meaning, or almost the same meaning, as the word in bold type.

1. **outskirts** of town

   A. business district   C. suburbs
   B. parks   D. wide streets

2. don't laugh at her **deformity**

   A. crippled look   C. joke
   B. funny face   D. misfortune

3. **lyrics** that are easy to remember

   A. dreams   C. musical verse
   B. features of a   D. vocabulary
       person

4. saw the **memorandum**

   A. great perfor-   C. note
      mance
   B. main event   D. strange creature

5. a famous **locality**

   A. location   C. person
   B. novel   D. reputation

(6–10) Choose the word or phrase with the **opposite** meaning, or with the meaning which is most nearly opposite.

6. trash **removal**

   A. addition   C. separate pile
   B. good smell   D. small load

7. job **requirement**

   A. failure   C. poor surroundings
   B. future   D. something that isn't
                         necessary

8. **reliance on** others

   A. dislike of   C. lack of respect for
   B. independence   D. refusal to take part
      from   with

9. to correct your **inability**

   A. ability   C. perfection
   B. good deed   D. success

10. filled with *hazards*

    A. polite remarks   C. safe features
    B. rich people   D. suckers

(11–15) Fill in the missing word in the sentence.

11. I admire his self- _____. Give him a job, and he finds a way to get it done.

    A. deformity   C. reliance
    B. inability   D. removal

12. Having 12 toes is a strange _____, but one that is not unheard of.

    A. deformity   C. inability
    B. hazard   D. removal

13. I'll write the music, you write the _____.

    A. locality   C. memorandum
    B. lyrics   D. requirement

14. It is a few miles east of San Antonio, in one of those shopping centers in the _____.

    A. locality   C. memorandum
    B. lyrics   D. outskirts

15. You will have to overcome many _____ in starting a business.

    A. deformities   C. localities
    B. hazards   D. memorandums

B. Nouns with Longer Definitions

coincidence   A pair of unexpected events that seem related but that actually occur purely by chance. Or, more generally, anything that happens unexpectedly or by chance.

corporation   A type of business organization. A corporation can have many owners, each with a certain number of "shares" in the business. One of the advantages of a corporation is that the business itself is responsible for debts; the owners have only a limited responsibility, or none at all.

dictator   A ruler who has absolute power, often one who rules in a cruel, wicked manner.

probability   The chances (good or bad) of something happening.

reduction   Making something smaller, or making a smaller copy of something.

specification   (often used in the plural) A full, detailed plan, particularly the exact plans and measurements for something being built.

summary   A brief account of what happened, or of information contained elsewhere.

survivor   A person who stays alive when others die, or who lives despite difficult conditions. In particular, a relative of a person who has just died.

variation	A change, a different version. In particular, a different version of a musical piece.
veto	Refusal, saying no to something. In particular, the right of the President to refuse to allow acts of Congress to become law. Governors also have *"veto power."* That is, they can refuse to allow acts of their legislatures to become state law. (Also used as a verb, *"to veto."*)

(1–5) Choose the word or phrase with the **same** meaning, or almost the same meaning, as the word in bold type.

1. the **specifications** for the new house

   A. drawings and details   C. money

   B. lumber and other materials   D. occupants

2. became a **dictator**

   A. lawyer   C. supporter

   B. opponent   D. tyrant

3. the **probability** of success

   A. cause   C. likelihood

   B. kind   D. result

4. officer of the **corporation**

   A. club   C. national political group

   B. military unit   D. jointly owned enterprise

5. write a **summary**

   A. job application   C. poem

   B. novel   D. short explanation

(6–10) Choose the word or phrase with the **opposite** meaning, or with the meaning which is most nearly opposite.

6. a **veto** of the bill

   A. amendment   C. payment

   B. approval   D. preparation

7. a huge **reduction**

   A. enlargement   C. statue

   B. savings   D. undertaking

8. a **survivor** of the accident

   A. cause   C. victim

   B. report   D. witness

9. a strange **coincidence**

   A. creative force   C. philosophy

   B. detective story   D. planned event

10. a striking **variation**

    A. appearance   C. plot

    B. development   D. sameness

(11–15) Fill in the missing word in the sentence.

11. What is the _____ of Mom's getting that new job?

    A. coincidence   C. summary

    B. probability   D. variation

12. General Motors is one of the largest _____ in the world.

    A. corporations   C. summaries

    B. reductions   D. variations

13. Can you give me a 50% _____ of that picture so that it will fit at the bottom of this page?

    A. coincidence   C. specification

    B. reduction   D. summary

14. Adolf Hitler was one of the worst
_____ in history.

A. corporations   C. survivors

B. dictators   D. variations

15. Why does Marilyn have _____ power over every movie I suggest?

A. probability   C. variation

B. summary   D. veto

C. Definitions for You to Derive from Context

Each of the words in this lesson can be used as either a noun or a verb. In each case, the noun and the verb meanings are similar.

1. **ban**

   The city has decided to **ban** trucks on Main Street from 9 to 5 on Saturdays. No trucks will be allowed on the street, even to make deliveries or pick-ups.

   A. charge a   C. drive
       parking fee

   B. direct   D. prohibit

2. opposite of the noun **ban**

   A. depth   C. permission

   B. emptiness   D. savings

3. **barricade**

   The rebels made a **barricade** 6 to 10 feet high of rocks, sandbags, wrecked furniture, and whatever else they could find to block the entrance to the town.

   A. message to the   C. request
       people

   B. protective wall   D. weapon

4. If you decided to **barricade** your room, what would be the purpose?

   A. to clean it up   C. to let air in

   B. to keep people   D. to make it sound-
       out   proof

5. **brawl**

   It was an old-fashioned **brawl**. Everyone in the bar was kicking and screaming and hitting each other.

   A. conversation   C. noisy fight

   B. drink   D. unusual story

6. Where would you most often see **brawling**?

   A. boxing ring   C. music studio

   B. library   D. principal's office

7. **clamor**

   Everyone in the convention hall was yelling for Mr. Wilson to resign. The **clamor** was deafening.

   A. betting   C. loud shouting

   B. discovery   D. stupid decision

8. opposite of the verb **to clamor**

   A. to finish   C. to keep quiet

   B. to join   D. to try to convince

9. **convict**

   All three members of the gang were **convicted** of murder and sentenced to long terms in prison.

   A. educated   C. lost

   B. found guilty   D. sent on their way

10. Where are you most likely to find **convicts**?

    A. doctor's office   C. school

    B. prison   D. the beach

11. **duplicate**

    Mary's new dress is almost a **duplicate** of the one I wore last Saturday. The only difference is that Mary's has a blue collar.

    A. exact copy   C. large size

    B. item of clothing   D. purchase

69

12. If your teacher **duplicates** a test, he or she

    A. hides it   C. rewrites it

    B. takes it   D. runs off copies

13. **embrace**

Mr. Fiedler was waiting for his daughter at the train station. When she stepped off the train, he gave her a warm **embrace**.

    A. bawling out   C. set of bags

    B. hug   D. ticket

14. Which two people are most likely to **embrace** each other?

    A. a salesman and   C. pilot and passenger
       a customer

    B. man and wife   D. two people talking to
                       each other by phone

15. **imprint**

The words she spoke to me have been **imprinted** in my memory forever.

    A. altered   C. made to last

    B. clouded   D. spared

16. The verb **imprint** can mean

    A. printed on   B. not printed

17. **quake**

Jeremy was so scared he was **quaking** in his boots. You could even hear his teeth chatter.

    A. crazy behavior   C. pain

    B. loud applause   D. violent shaking

18. The noun **quake** is often used as a short form of

    A. earthquake   C. quaker

    B. quackery   D. quicken

19. **sponsor**

We asked several businesses in town to **sponsor** the Little League baseball teams.

    A. attend   C. play against

    B. lend support to   D. write about

20. Who are the **sponsors** of a TV show?

    A. actors   C. producers

    B. advertisers   D. viewers

D. Nouns for You to Look Up in the Dictionary

(1–5) Each of the nouns in bold type has to do with the military, at least in part of its definition. Unless you are sure you know the word's meaning, look it up. Then choose the word or phrase with a similar meaning.

1. an army **brigade**

    A. rank   C. unit

    B. uniform   D. weapon

2. a **cavalry** soldier

    A. a marine   C. an officer

    B. an enlisted man   D. a soldier on
                            horseback

3. tell it to the **chaplain**

    A. commanding   C. military priest, minis-
       officer   ter, or rabbi

    B. master sergeant   D. soldier who sends
                            and receives mes-
                            sages by radio

4. in *civilian* clothes

  A. Air Force   C. dress uniform
  B. army fatigues   D. not military

5. granted a *furlough*

  A. award   C. new assignment
  B. leave of   D. promotion
     absence
     from duty

(6–7) Answer the following questions.

6. When was the *cavalry* an important type of fighting unit?

  A. the Civil War   C. the Vietnam War
  B. The Korean War

7. What is one of the main jobs of a *chaplain*?

  A. helping soldiers C. making weapons
     with their
     problems
  B. leading units   D. planning military
     into battle   campaigns

(8–10) Fill in the missing word in the sentence.

8. A _____ consists of several battalions.

  A. brigade   C. civilian
  B. cavalry   D. furlough

10. The Armed Forces employ _____ for many office jobs.

  A. brigades   C. civilians
  B. chaplains   D. furloughs

9. Soldiers often receive a _____ at Christmas.

  A. brigade   C. civilian
  B. chaplain   D. furlough

═══════════════════════════

E. Words with More than One Meaning

All the words in this unit can be used as nouns, sometimes with different meanings. Some can also be used as other parts of speech.

eclipse
    a. [*verb*] To surpass.
    b. [*noun*] Being surpassed.
    c. [*noun*] An occurrence where the moon gets in the way of the sun's rays (solar *eclipse*) or the moon is put in shadow by the earth (lunar *eclipse*).

fore
    a. [*noun*] Something that came before. Or front position.
    b. [*adjective*] Former, coming before.
    c. [*interjection*] The warning call of a golfer to tell other people to watch out when he is about to hit the ball.

identity
    a. [*noun*] Sameness.
    b. [*noun*] The basic character and personality of a person.

multiple   a. [*noun*] A number you can get by multiplying a particular number by another number. For example, 28 is a **multiple** of 7. So is 21.

b. [*adjective*] Many, or at least more than one.

static   a. [*noun*] Crackling noise in radio reception, caused by such things as bad weather or electrical inteference.

b. [*adjective*] At rest, showing little change.

c. [*adjective*] A form of electricity or electrical charge.

(1–4) Choose the word or phrase with the **same** meaning, or almost the same meaning, as the word in bold type.

1. **eclipse** of the moon

   A. darkening   C. special quality
   B. path   D. study

2. a **static** situation

   A. critical   C. unchanged
   B. dangerous   D. wildly romantic

3. loss of **identity**

   A. comfort   C. shame
   B. knowing who   D. spare part
      you are

4. **multiple** injuries

   A. healed   C. painful
   B. of the head   D. several

(5–7) Choose the word or phrase with the **opposite** meaning, or with the meaning which is most nearly opposite.

5. radio **static**

   A. clean sound   C. old program
   B. good show   D. weak station

6. in the **fore** section

   A. above   C. enlarged
   B. behind   D. inside

7. an **eclipsed** record

   A. accurate   C. unbeaten
   B. pleasant   D. very slow

(8–9) Fill in the missing word in the sentence.

8. Is 96 a(n) _____ of 16?

   A. eclipse   C. identity
   B. fore   D. multiple

9. We share a(n) _____ of purpose.

   A. eclipse   C. multiple
   B. identity   D. static

(10) Pick out the best sentence to go with the definition.

10. golfer's warning

    A. Andrea has come to the **fore** as one of our best fund raisers.
    B. Didn't you hear me when I yelled, "**Fore**"?
    C. Ask for a seat in one of the **fore** sections of the airplane.

F. Words with the Prefix *Con-*

The prefix *con-* means "with" or "together." *Con-* also appears in the forms *col-*, *com-*, and *cor-*, depending on the first letter of the word to which the prefix is attached.

collide   [*verb*] To bang together (as when two items *collide*) or to smash into (*to collide with* another object). From *con-* + *lide*, which comes from a Latin word meaning "to injure by hitting."

confederate   [*noun*] Ally. Or (capitalized), in the American Civil War, a person on the Southern, or *Confederate*, side. *Confederate* comes from *con-* + *federate*, which means "to unite."

confidential   [*adjective*] Private, secret. From *con-* + *fide*, a form of the Latin word meaning "to trust." Something *confidential* is something that has been trusted to you to take care of.

consequence   [*noun*] The result of an action. Or the conclusion you draw from a set of facts. Or more generally, importance. From *con* + *sequence*, which comes from the Latin word meaning "to follow."

consequently   [*adverb*] Following as a result. From *consequence* (above).

(1–3) Choose the word or phrase with the **same** meaning, or almost the same meaning, as the word in bold type.

1. a person of **consequence**

   A. beauty   C. significance
   B. intelligence   D. strength

2. **consequently**, we had to

   A. nevertheless   C. particularly
   B. on the whole   D. therefore

3. the bicycles **collided**

   A. hit each other C. were destroyed
   B. rode together   D. were sold

(4–6) Choose the word or phrase with the **opposite** meaning, or with the meaning which is most nearly opposite.

4. a **confederate** of the gang

   A. enemy   C. purpose
   B. member   D. loot

5. a **confidential** report

   A. difficult to   C. public
      understand
   B. disappointing   D. thrilling

6. opposite of **consequently**

   A. nevertheless   C. particularly
   B. on the whole   D. therefore

(7–10) Answer the following questions.

7. Which of these states was on the **Confederate** side in the Civil War?

   A. Massachusetts   C. New York
   B. Michigan   D. Virginia

8. Which word below has the same part of speech as **consequence**?

   A. collide   C. confidential
   B. confederate   D. consequently

9. The word **collide** is often used to describe events involving

    A. ballpoint pens   C. hair
    B. cars   D. ribbons

10. The U.S. Government marks some written documents **confidential**. Why?

    A. they are considered good examples of writing style
    B. they are mailed to thousands of people
    C. they are of no consequence
    D. they contain secret information

G. Chapter 6 Review

(1–7) Choose the word or phrase with the **same** meaning, or almost the same meaning, as the word in bold type.

1. the President's **veto**

   A. popularity   C. refusal to sign
   B. program   D. victory

2. happened **by coincidence**

   A. as a result of a plan   C. for unhappy reasons
   B. by chance   D. with assistance

3. a **reduction** in rent

   A. equivalent   C. payment
   B. lowering   D. portion

4. the sole **survivor**

   A. encounter   C. reason
   B. person still alive D. supporter

5. a small **variation**

   A. change   C. group
   B. hole   D. skin problem

6. **requirement** for success

   A. desire   C. plan
   B. necessity   D. wishes

7. avoid the **hazard**

   A. confusion   C. obstacle
   B. extra cost   D. policeman

(8–12) Choose the word or phrase with the **opposite** meaning, or with the meaning which is most nearly opposite.

8. **convicted** of a crime

   A. found not guilty C. not certain
   B. not a victim   D. received the benefit

9. a **civilian** employee

   A. foreign   C. military
   B. high-level   D. unsuccessful

10. a perfect **duplicate**

    A. legal act   C. original
    B. miss   D. person who is not fooled

11. the cars **collided**

    A. avoided each other   C. started up
    B. slowed down   D. were sold

12. as a **consequence**

    A. cause   C. remedy
    B. penalty   D. serious matter

(13–17) Fill in the missing word in the sentence.

13. Soldiers in the _____ rode on horses.
    A. barricade   C. cavalry
    B. brigade   D. corporation

14. My brother is coming home on _____ from the Air Force during the Christmas holidays.
    A. embrace   C. imprint
    B. furlough   D. reliance

15. They live on the _____ of Chicago.
    A. deformity   C. outskirts
    B. locality   D. specification

16. Can you remember the _____ of that old Beatles song "I Want to Hold Your Hand"?
    A. lyrics   C. quake
    B. memorandum   D. summary

17. There is a _____ in our town on the sale of alcoholic drinks after midnight.
    A. ban   C. probability
    B. brawl   D. sponsor

(18–19) Choose the word that has the two meanings that are in bold type.

18. *result of multiplication*; *many*
    A. gross   C. multiple
    B. majority   D. product

19. *sameness*; *basic character of a person*
    A. equality   C. individuality
    B. identity   D. personality

(20) Pick out the best sentence to go with the definition.

20. unchanged
    A. Can't you tune in that radio better? There's too much *static*.
    B. The results over the past three years have been *static*.
    C. The sparks you get when you run those two pieces of material together are a form of *static* electricity.

(21) Answer the following question.

21. What does the prefix *col-* in *collide* mean?
    A. away   C. together
    B. over   D. without

(22) Look carefully at the pair of words in capitals. Try to figure out the relationship between them. Then choose the sentence that does the **best** job of showing how the words are related.

22. OUTSKIRTS : CITY
    A. The outskirts surround a city.
    B. The city surrounds the outskirts.
    C. The outskirts and the city go together.

75

(23–25) Figure out how the first two words in capitals are related to each other. Then choose the pair of words below it that are related in the same way.

23. OUTSKIRTS : CITY

    A. FRAME : PAINTING
    B. PAINTING : FRAME
    C. PART : WHOLE

24. PROHIBIT : BAN

    A. INSTRUCT : TEACH
    B. MAKE : USE
    C. STOP : GO

25. BRIGADE : SOLDIERS

    A. TEAM : MANAGER
    B. TEAM : PLAYERS
    C. TEAM : VICTORY

CHAPTER 7.

Words in this chapter:

ambassador
artery

barbarian
broker

camouflage
coma
cordial
corporal
courtship

discharge
dishonor
dispatch
disrespect
distribution

efficiency
embassy
emerald
epidemic

forestry
forgery

gill
graft

identification
incense
insulation

maestro
maximum
minimum
morgue
multitude

observatory
occupant
occurrence

paralysis
passport
pneumonia
possibility
privacy
profile

rarity
rheumatism
rivet

slander
survival

tariff

A. Nouns with Simple Definitions

efficiency	effective way of doing things, without waste
maximum	the most (also used as an adjective)
minimum	the least (also used as an adjective)
multitude	a great number, particularly of people
occupant	resident
occurrence	happening
possibility	something that is possible
privacy	being alone, not being bothered by other people
rarity	something very uncommon
survival	something left over; staying alive

(1–5) Choose the word or phrase with the **same** meaning, or almost the same meaning, as the word in bold type.

1. the *maximum* allowed

    A. highest amount
    B. lowest amount

2. the *minimum* allowed

    A. highest amount
    B. lowest amount

3. in the midst of the *multitude*

    A. battle   C. crowd
    B. circle   D. flow

4. a strange *occurrence*

    A. event   C. flavor
    B. feeling   D. growth

5. the *occupant* of the house

    A. dweller   C. layout
    B. kitchen   D. roof

(6–10) Choose the word or phrase with the **opposite** meaning, or with the meaning which is most nearly opposite.

6. in the *privacy* of the home

    A. being surround- C. upstairs
       ed by people
    B. outside   D. weakness

7. an event that is a *rarity*

    A. happy affair   C. strange happening
    B. ordinary thing D. very expensive
                         matter

8. done with *efficiency*

    A. anger   C. the help of others
    B. speed   D. wastefulness

9. the *survival* of the fittest

    A. death   C. ugliness
    B. growth   D. weakness

10. a distant *possibility*

    A. something hid-   C. something that can't
       den from view   be done
    B. something mov-   D. something you want
       ing away from   to happen
       you

(11–15) Fill in the missing word in the sentence.

11. On your first job, your salary may only be the _____ allowed by the government.

    A. efficiency   C. minimum
    B. maximum   D. survival

12. Your _____ in a highway accident may depend on whether or not you use seat belts.

    A. efficiency   C. minimum
    B. maximum   D. survival

13. When you are surrounded by a *multitude* of people, you don't have any _____.

    A. efficiency   C. privacy
    B. possibility   D. rarity

14. It is a(n) _____ to find turtles like that in this part of the country.

    A. efficiency   C. privacy
    B. occupant   D. rarity

15. The former _____ of this home was a captain in the Army.

    A. efficiency   C. privacy
    B. occupant   D. survival

B. Nouns with Longer Definitions

barbarian	A person who is not civilized. Also [*adjective*] acting with very poor manners, or acting very crudely and cruelly.
broker	An agent who brings buyers and sellers together, or who arranges things. For example, there are real estate **brokers**, **brokers** who help you buy stocks and bonds, marriage **brokers**, etc.
camouflage	The disguise of equipment, as in war, to make it hard for the enemy to identify. Also, [*verb*] to hide, to disguise the appearance of.
gill	In fish and other animals that live in the water, an organ that is used to get oxygen from the water.
observatory	A place with telescopes set up to look at the distant skies, stars, planets, and so on.
paralysis	Being unable to move a particular part of your body; the type of condition that sometimes results from an accident or from suffering a stroke. Also, in general, powerlessness, not being able to take needed action.

passport   A little book the government issues to allow you to travel to foreign countries.

rivet   A pin or a bolt with a head on it which you use to fasten two pieces together by passing it through a hole and then flattening out the other end so it also has a head. Also, [*verb*] to fasten together with a **rivet**, or more generally, simply to fasten firmly.

slander   Statements that are false and damage someone's reputation. In law, **slander** is an offense which can serve as the basis of a lawsuit. **Slander** can also be used as a verb meaning "to tell lies about someone."

tariff   The fee you pay to bring goods into a country. Or the schedule of rates for train fares, telephone charges, electricity fees, etc.

(1–3) Choose the word or phrase with the **same** meaning, or almost the same meaning, as the word in bold type.

1. **tariff** on Japanese goods

   A. duty
   B. freight
   C. insurance
   D. label

2. insurance **broker**

   A. benefit
   B. coverage
   C. policy
   D. salesperson

3. college's **observatory**

   A. fees
   B. lookout
   C. place where students live
   D. policy

(4–8) Choose the word or phrase with the **opposite** meaning, or with the meaning which is most nearly opposite.

4. to **slander** Mrs. Forster

   A. accompany
   B. assist
   C. dislike
   D. tell the truth about

5. **barbarian** habits

   A. effective
   B. practical
   C. refined
   D. weird

6. result in **paralysis**

   A. a larger family
   B. a slowdown
   C. freedom to act
   D. the unexpected

7. **camouflaged** soldier

   A. cowardly
   B. friendly
   C. veteran
   D. visible

8. **riveted** in place

   A. buried
   B. hidden
   C. loose
   D. standing

(9–10) Answer the following questions.

9. When do you need a **passport**?

   A. to fly
   B. to enter college
   C. to go to Dallas
   D. to travel to France

10. Which of the following animals has **gills**?

   A. buffalo
   B. rat
   C. robin
   D. shark

(11–15) Fill in the missing word in the sentence.

11. Alex uses a wheelchair because of the _____ in his legs.

   A. gill
   B. paralysis
   C. rivet
   D. slander

12. Melanie made it sound like she just loves Latin, but she was _____ her true feelings.

   A. brokering
   B. camouflaging
   C. riveting
   D. slandering

80

13. Have you seen the new schedule of
_____ for the State Line Bus
Company?

A. gills   C. rivets
B. passports   D. tariffs

14. If you use a(n) _____ to sell
your house, you will have to pay a fee.

A. barbarian   C. observatory
B. broker   D. passport

15. I think Seth is a(n) _____ the
way he always beats up his little sister.

A. barbarian   C. paralysis
B. observatory   D. slander

C. Definitions for You to Derive from Context

Read the sentence following the word in bold type and on the basis of what you read, choose the correct definition.

1. **ambassador**
The President discussed the matter with
the German *ambassador*. He felt the issue
was so important that it could only be discussed with Germany's highest ranking
representative to the United States.

A. a country's   C. a foreign visitor
   official represent-
   ative to another
   country
B. a dictator   D. a general

2. Where do you think *ambassadors* to the
United States live?

A. Alaska   C. the South
B. Maine   D. Washington, D.C.

3. **courtship**
It was a long *courtship*. He did everything
he could to get her to like him.

A. actions aimed   C. race
   at gaining some-
   one's favor or
   love
B. becoming king   D. view from the top of
   or queen   a mountain

4. *Courtship* usually means to try to

A. get someone to   C. recover from a
   marry you   sickness
B. hold on to your   D. start the car
   money

5. **embassy**
Most countries put up large and expensive
embassies in the capitals of foreign countries so that their representatives can live
and do their work in surroundings that
make a good impression.

A. bridge   C. factory making
                        products for sale
                        overseas
B. building for the D. football stadium
   official represen-
   tatives of a for-
   eign country

6. Who lives in an *embassy*?

A. a business   C. an officer in the
   person   army
B. an ambassador   D. a priest

81

7. **emerald**

Her necklace had an *emerald* in the middle surrounded by diamonds.

A. precious stone   C. scarf

B. scar   D. TV

8. The word *emerald* can also refer to the color of emeralds, which is somewhat like the color of grass when it has just come out in the spring.

A. black   C. flaming red

B. deep blue   D. yellow green

9. **forestry**

People who study *forestry* get jobs managing our great national forests or working for lumber companies with large forest holdings.

A. a foreign   C. cliffs used for
    language   climbing

B. a kind of sport   D. study of how to take
                       care of forests

10. When you think of *forestry*, you think of

A. cars   C. the ocean

B. house cats   D. trees

11. **forgery**

The signature on that check is a *forgery*. It's my name, and it looks like my signature. But I didn't sign it.

A. crime of driving   C. crime of picking
    while drunk   someone's pocket

B. crime of holding   D. crime of signing
    up a bank   someone else's
                    name

12. Some paintings are *forgeries*. What do you think this means?

A. they are made   C. they are unfinished
    to look like the
    works of famous
    artists

B. they are of very   D. they are very
    poor quality   modern

13. **incense**

Jean had bought some sticks of *incense*. While we were sitting around after dinner, we lit one of the sticks. It gave off a wonderful odor.

A. raging fire   C. substance you burn
                     to make a pleasing
                     smell

B. lumber for build-   D. trees in the woods
    ing furniture

14. How might you describe the smell of *incense*?

A. bitter   C. like the fumes from
                    an old truck

B. like rotten eggs   D. sweet

15. **insulation**

There are different kinds of *insulation*. There is the kind you put in walls to keep the heat in. There is the kind you put around wires so you don't get a shock when you touch them. And so on.

A. decoration   C. kind of metal used
                     in electrical wiring

B. hole   D. protective covering

16. Where else might you use *insulation*?

A. as a way of   C. to kill bugs
    measuring things

B. for sound proof-   D. to make your car
    ing   run better

17. **maestro**

The *maestro* turned to the audience, put his baton down, and took a bow. Then the members of the orchestra rose and also took a bow.

A. member of the   C. person with a very
    audience   high voice

B. orchestra leader   D. writer of music

18. *Maestros* have to be

A. college gradu-   C. musicians
    ates

B. millionaires   D. U.S. citizens

19. **morgue**

The *morgue* is an interesting place, but it's not a place you would have fun visiting. It has bodies lined up. In some cases they are waiting to be identified before burial. In other cases, such as murders, for example, they are waiting to be studied to help solve the crimes.

A. cemetery   C. police station

B. place that holds   D. scene of the crime
    dead bodies

20. What do you think of when you think of a *morgue*?

A. a Christmas   C. math lessons
    vacation

B. death   D. sunny hillsides

D. Nouns for You to Look Up in the Dictionary

(1–5) Each of the nouns in bold type has to do with medicine, at least in part of its definition. Unless you are sure you know the word's meaning, look it up. Then choose the word or phrase with a similar meaning.

1. cut the *artery*

A. major blood   C. part of
    vessel   the lungs

B. muscle in   D. stomach tissue
    the chest

2. came out of a *coma*

A. deadly germ   C. device for holding
                  a broken bone
                  in place

B. deep state of   D. high fever
    unconsciousness

3. afraid of an *epidemic*

A. removal of an   C. sores on the skin
    arm or a leg

B. spread of a   D. type of cancer
    disease

4. died from *pneumonia*

A. brain tumor   C. loss of blood

B. heart disease   D. lung infection

5. terrible *rheumatism*

A. a particular type   C. heart condition
    of high blood
    pressure

B. cough   D. old-fashioned word
            for arthritis

(6–8) Answer the following questions.

6. What is one of the worst effects of *pneumonia*?

A. heavy coughing   C. sores on the skin

B. loss of hair   D. upset stomach

7. Where do you get pain when you have *rheumatism*?

A. eyes   C. stomach

B. joints   D. teeth

8. In what direction does an **artery** carry blood?

    A. away from the heart

    B. toward the heart

(9–10) Fill in the missing word in the sentence.

9. A(n) _____ of the flu killed millions of people at the end of World War I.

    A. artery   C. epidemic

    B. coma   D. pneumonia

10. The cause of a(n) _____ can be either sickness or injury.

    A. artery   C. pneumonia

    B. coma

E. Words with More than One Meaning

Some of the words in this lesson have two or more different meanings as nouns. Others have different meanings depending upon whether they are used as nouns or adjectives.

cordial
    a. [*noun*] A type of alcoholic drink that is usually very strong and often sweet and is served just before or after dinner.
    b. [*adjective*] Very warm and friendly.

corporal
    a. [*noun*] A rank in the army (above a private but below a sergeant).
    b. [*adjective*] Bodily. Often used in the expression "**corporal** punishment," which refers to such types of punishment as whipping, or even death.

graft
    a. [*noun*] An illegal payoff made to obtain special favors from a public official or a person working for a business.
    b. [*noun*] Outside matter or tissue which has been implanted into a living body. (Also *verb*, to make such an implant.)

identification
    a. [*noun*] Evidence of who you are.
    b. [*noun*] Finding who or what something is.
    c. [*noun*] Feeling of closeness to a cause or a person or a point of view.

profile
    a. [*noun*] Side view of a figure, particularly when it is shown in outline form.
    b. [*noun*] A brief biography.

(1–5) Choose the word or phrase with the **same** meaning, or almost the same meaning, as the word in bold type.

1. a brief **profile**

    A. attempt   C. explosion

    B. description   D. play

2. accepts **graft**

    A. money   C. the honor

    B. responsibility   D. visitors

3. the process of *identification*

    A. betrayal   C. discovery

    B. cleaning   D. drift

4. *corporal* concerns

    A. having to do   C. pressing
       with a person

    B. holy   D. sweet

5. a *cordial* greeting

    A. announced   C. formed

    B. cheerful   D. loud

(6–7) Answer the following questions.

6. Which of the following is a form of *corporal* punishment?

    A. bawling out   C. jail sentence

    B. fine   D. spanking

7. On which of the following are *grafts* sometimes made?

    A. exams   C. kitchen equipment

    B. fruit trees   D. novels

(8–10) Fill in the missing word in the sentence.

8. Have the police made a positive _____?

    A. cordial   C. graft

    B. corporal   D. identification

9. Orlando's fat stomach and pointy chin give him a funny _____.

    A. cordial   C. identification

    B. graft   D. profile

10. They served _____ to the guests.

    A. cordials   C. grafts

    B. corporals   D. profiles

F. Words with the Prefix *Dis-*

The prefix *dis-* means "not" or "opposite of," and sometimes "do the opposite of."

discharge   a. [*verb*] To release, to let go. For example, to release from the army.

                b. [*noun*] Permission to leave the army. Also: The firing (release of the trigger) of a gun; being fired (released) from a job; the release of electrical current; the oozing out of pus from a sore.—Any release. *Discharge* comes from *dis- + charge*, that is, not to charge and therefore to release.

dishonor   [*verb*] To cause someone to lose honor. From *dis- + honor*, that is, not to honor. Also, [*noun*] shame, the loss of honor.

dispatch   a. [*verb*] To send out speedily and efficiently. From *dis- + patch*, which comes from a Latin word meaning "to hinder."

                b. [*noun*] Getting rid of something, even killing someone, quickly and efficiently. Also, a message or news item, particularly one sent in war. In general, speed and efficiency. (Sometimes spelled *despatch*.)

disrespect   [*noun*] Lack of respect.

distribution a. [*noun*] The act of giving out or giving away something.

b. [*noun*] In business, shipping goods.

c. [*noun*] In natural sciences, the pattern of how things occur over an area, such as the **distribution** of a particular type of animal in parts of North America.

Distribution comes from **dis-** + **tribute**. Since a **tribute** is a payment made by many people to a king or other ruler, a **distribution** goes in the opposite direction, to many people.

(1–5) Choose the word or phrase with the **same** meaning, or almost the same meaning, as the word in bold type.

1. You have **dishonored** your family

   A. disgraced them   C. joined them for a family event
   B. helped them make a living   D. left them

2. do it with **dispatch**

   A. firmness   C. loving care
   B. gracefulness   D. quickness

3. **discharged** his rifle

   A. carried   C. loaded
   B. cleaned   D. shot

4. showing total **disrespect**

   A. lack of courtesy   C. lack of knowledge
   B. lack of feeling   D. lack of skill

5. **distribution** to the poor

   A. giving   C. showing
   B. selling   D. telling

(6–8) Choose the word or phrase with the **opposite** meaning, or with the meaning which is most nearly opposite.

6. **discharge from** a job

   A. being hired for   C. not being paid for
   B. looking for   D. refusing

7. total **disrespect**

   A. feeling of loss   C. show of admiration
   B. greed   D. stupidity

8. afraid it might **dishonor**

   A. accept   C. honor
   B. attempt   D. refuse

(9–10) Fill in the missing word in the sentence.

9. Our local newspaper was the first one to receive a _____ about the battle.

   A. discharge   C. disrespect
   B. dispatch   D. distribution

10. What kind of _____ system does your company have for shipping out all those orders?

   A. discharge   C. disrespect
   B. dispatch   D. distribution

G. Chapter 7 Review

(1–7) Choose the word or phrase with the **same** meaning, or almost the same meaning, as the word in bold type.

1. a matter of *survival*
   - A. common sense
   - B. enjoying the scene
   - C. playfulness
   - D. staying alive

2. a clever *camouflage*
   - A. disguise
   - B. ending
   - C. story
   - D. trick

3. total *paralysis*
   - A. being unable to move
   - B. involvement
   - C. lack of understanding
   - D. nonsense

4. guilty of *slander*
   - A. a minor crime
   - B. assault
   - C. cheating
   - D. false statements

5. *riveted* together
   - A. bolted
   - B. grown
   - C. seen
   - D. traveled

6. find it a *rarity*
   - A. greedy demand
   - B. insulting remark
   - C. uncommon thing
   - D. unfinished piece of business

7. in the camp of the *barbarians*
   - A. officers
   - B. railroad workers
   - C. supermen
   - D. uncivilized people

(8–12) Choose the word or phrase with the **opposite** meaning, or with the meaning which is most nearly opposite.

8. *distribution* of products
   - A. large number
   - B. receiving
   - C. rejection
   - D. use

9. a *maximum* charge
   - A. expected
   - B. favorable
   - C. minimum
   - D. unfair

10. *dispatch* a messenger
    - A. hire
    - B. lose
    - C. receive
    - D. talk to

11. a *multitude* of sins
    - A. avoidance
    - B. disapproval
    - C. former acts
    - D. small number

12. nothing but a *forgery*
    - A. expensive matter
    - B. important message
    - C. real thing
    - D. something done on purpose

(13–17) Fill in the missing word in the sentence.

13. Do you need a(n) _____ to go to Mexico?
    - A. ambassador
    - B. embassy
    - C. passport
    - D. tariff

14. The reason my grandmother's fingers are all twisted and swollen is that she has _____.
    - A. artery
    - B. coma
    - C. pneumonia
    - D. rheumatism

15. I like that ring in the window with the huge _____ in the middle.
    - A. emerald
    - B. epidemic
    - C. insulation
    - D. observatory

16. And now we present the _____ himself, John Smidgens, the leader of the band.
    - A. broker
    - B. gill
    - C. maestro
    - D. occupant

17. The murdered woman's body was sent to the _____.

A. courtship
B. forestry
C. incense
D. morgue

(18–19) Choose the word that has the two meanings that are in bold type.

18. *rank in the army*; *bodily*

A. corporal
B. general
C. major
D. physical

19. *warm and friendly*; *type of drink*

A. cordial
B. hearty
C. liqueur
D. refreshment

(20) Pick out the best sentence to go with the definition.

20. illegal payoff

A. Did they do a skin *graft?*
B. None of our public officials takes *graft*.
C. They use a *graft* to get the kind of apple tree they want.

(21) Answer the following question.

21. What does the prefix *dis-* in *discharge* mean?

A. against
B. definitely
C. not
D. visible

(22) Look carefully at the pair of words in capitals. Try to figure out the relationship between them. Then choose the sentence that does the **best** job of showing how the words are related.

22. EMERALD : JEWEL

A. An emerald is a kind of jewel.
B. An emerald is more than a jewel.
C. An emerald looks like a jewel.

(23–25) Figure out how the first two words in capitals are related to each other. Then choose the pair of words below it that are related in the same way.

23. EMERALD : JEWEL

A. SONG : MUSICIAN
B. GRASS : ROCK
C. TROUT : FISH

24. MAESTRO : ORCHESTRA

A. GENERAL : ADMIRAL
B. GENERAL : ARMY
C. GENERAL : WAR

25. GILL : FISH

A. LUNG : AIR
B. LUNG : BREATHING
C. LUNG : PERSON

CHAPTER 8.

Words in this chapter:

ammonia
applicant
arson
asbestos

blotter

chime
clutter
curfew
custody

defendant
devout

edible
excess
exterior

finances
flounder
frolic
function

infantile
investment

jovial

logic

mangle
molar

overcast

pastel
pawn
persistence
pollen
procession
prolong
proposition
proverb
provoke

recruit
refresh
relapse
relish
repetition
reproduce
retain

sterling

transform
transmit
tuition

A. Nouns with Simple Definitions

applicant	a person who applies for a job, or for something else
defendant	a person who has been sued or brought to trial for a crime
excess	more than enough, too much
exterior	the outside area (or, *adjective*, outside)
finances	(plural) money supplies
frolic	fun and merriment (or, *verb*, to play happily)
investment	purchase made with the hope of income or profit
logic	reasoning
persistence	sticking at something, refusing to give up
sterling	silver (or, *adjective*, made of silver)

(1–5) Choose the word or phrase with the **same** meaning, or almost the same meaning, as the word in bold type.

1. to *frolic* in the park
   - A. destroy property
   - B. have a secret meeting
   - C. take part in joyful activity
   - D. walk with friends

2. the *exterior* wall
   - A. cement or brick
   - B. outer
   - C. supporting
   - D. unfinished

3. to apply *logic*
   - A. learning
   - B. skill
   - C. thinking
   - D. will

4. to do away with the *excess*
   - A. cheater
   - B. extra amount
   - C. making fun of someone
   - D. unfair charge

5. saw three *applicants*
   - A. customers
   - B. people looking for work
   - C. performers
   - D. public officials

(6–8) Choose the word or phrase with the **opposite** meaning, or with the meaning which is most nearly opposite.

6. a smart *investment*
   - A. defense
   - B. dishonest effort
   - C. dull speech
   - D. withdrawal of money

7. to show *persistence*
   - A. a bad quality
   - B. cleanliness
   - C. lack of will
   - D. strong desire

8. on behalf of the *defendant*
   - A. accuser
   - B. boss
   - C. older person
   - D. seller

(9–10) Answer the following questions.

9. What do you think British *sterling* might be?

   A. clothes   C. money
   B. food   D. type of plastic

10. Your personal *finances* have to do with how you

    A. earn and spend money   C. take care of your body
    B. feel about the world   D. treat your family

(11–15) Fill in the missing word in the sentence.

11. Life isn't all fun and _____.

    A. excess   C. logic
    B. frolic   D. persistence

12. My grandmother had that tea set. It's made of _____.

    A. exterior   C. investment
    B. finances   D. sterling

13. No one thought Linda would become such a good tennis player, but we didn't realize how much _____ she had.

    A. applicant   C. frolic
    B. excess   D. persistence

14. The _____ in the case is being sued by one of the passengers he had in his car when the accident took place.

    A. applicant   C. exterior
    B. defendant   D. investment

15. U.S. Government bonds are a very safe _____.

    A. exterior   C. investment
    B. excess   D. sterling

B. Nouns with Longer Definitions

ammonia   A very harsh-smelling gas which has many uses in industry. For example, it is used to make fertilizer and other chemicals. It is also used in refrigeration processes. The water solution of *ammonia* gas is also called *ammonia*; it is commonly used as a general household cleaner.

asbestos   A mineral which occurs in the form of long fibers. *Asbestos* used to be used widely in construction and manufacturing because it resists fire and chemical action. In recent years it has been discovered that it is a health hazard, so its use has been greatly reduced.

blotter   Something used to soak up ink or other liquid. *Blotters* are usually made of special thick paper.

curfew   A regulation that tells people they have to be off the street and inside at a certain hour of the night.

custody   Control and responsibility for another person. In cases of divorce, one of the parents is usually given *custody* of the children.

molar   One of the flat teeth you chew with at the sides and back of your mouth.

pastel — Any of a group of pale light colors. Also, a kind of artist's crayon, or a drawing made using *pastel* crayons.

pawn — In the game of chess, one of the eight small pieces each player has that start out in the row in front of the larger pieces. In general, a *pawn* is something of not very great value that is being used to obtain something more important.

pollen — The fine dust from flowers that fertilizes plants. Hay fever, which causes many people to sneeze and blow their noses in the summer, is a reaction to *pollen* in the air.

proverb — A short popular saying which is considered to contain a deep truth. "Haste makes waste" is a *proverb*.

(1–5) Choose the word or phrase with the **same** meaning, or almost the same meaning, as the word in bold type.

1. a set of *pastels*

    A. coloring sticks   C. keys
    B. hats   D. rings

2. a bottle of *ammonia*

    A. lemon juice   C. vitamin pills
    B. soda   D. window cleaner

3. *curfew* hour

    A. when you wake up   C. when school lets out
    B. noon   D. bedtime

4. *custody* of the children

    A. pictures of them   C. their diet
    B. right to raise them D. their education

5. in the old *proverb*

    A. part of town   C. words of wisdom
    B. picture   D. textbook

(6–10) Answer the following questions.

6. Which of the following produces *pollen*?

    A. car engines   C. roses
    B. cows   D. rushing water

7. Who might fix a damaged *molar*?

    A. airplane mechanic   C. dentist
    B. auto mechanic   D. surgeon

8. Where would you be most likely to use a *blotter*?

    A. in bed   C. on top of a chocolate cream pie
    B. in your hat   D. on your desk

9. How would you describe the job of working with *asbestos*?

    A. creative   C. fun
    B. dangerous   D. intelligent

10. If the first piece the white player in chess loses is a *pawn*, how many does he have left?

    A. seven   C. one
    B. four   D. none

(11–15) Fill in the missing word in the sentence.

11. Years ago, poor Uncle Frank put _____ in his walls as insulation; now he has had to spend a lot of money to have it removed.

    A. ammonia   C. blotters
    B. asbestos   D. pollen

12. Mother, do you have a(n) _____ to wipe up this bottle of ink that Jesse spilled on the kitchen table?

    A. blotter   C. pastel
    B. molar   D. pawn

13. The radio said the _____ count is very high today, but I haven't sneezed all morning.

    A. asbestos   C. pollen
    B. pastel   D. proverb

14. The soldiers were instructed to shoot anyone seen on the streets after the _____ hour of 11 at night.

    A. blotter   C. custody
    B. curfew   D. pastel

15. "Better late than never" is a _____.

    A. curfew   C. pastel
    B. custody   D. proverb

C. Definitions for You to Derive from Context

Read the sentence following the word in bold type and on the basis of what you read, choose the correct definition.

1. **arson**
   It looks to me like the cause of that fire that burned down the house was **arson**. There is no way that fire could have started by itself.

   A. damage from a   C. putting out a fire
      fire
   B. protecting   D. starting a fire with
      against a fire   evil intent

2. **Arson** is

   A. a crime   C. friendly
   B. amusing   D. often very helpful

3. **clutter**
   Your room is a mess. There is **clutter** all over the floor.

   A. furniture   C. paint
   B. litter   D. polish

4. opposite of **clutter**

   A. liquid   C. orderliness
   B. more space   D. silence

5. **devout**
   My father is a **devout** Christian. He believes in prayer and worship, and of course he goes to church regularly.

   A. different   C. tough
   B. good to one's   D. very religious
      family

6. opposite of **devout**

   A. amusing   C. gentle
   B. false   D. not believing in God

7. **edible**
   That mushroom is **edible**. You can eat it and you won't get sick.

   A. dolled-up   C. educated
   B. eatable   D. home-grown

93

8. What kinds of things are **edible**?

    A. air and soil   C. food

    B. facts   D. nuts and bolts

9. **infantile**

Don't be **infantile**. You're acting like your three-month-old sister.

    A. aggressive   C. lonely

    B. babyish   D. loving

10. The word **infantile** is derived from the word

    A. in   C. fan

    B. infant   D. tile

11. **jovial**

Why are you in such a **jovial** mood? You must think you're Santa Claus.

    A. cold   C. jolly

    B. fat   D. dressed in red

12. opposite of **jovial**

    A. lean   C. unhappy

    B. naked   D. warm

13. **overcast**

The weather is **overcast** this morning, but the clouds should lift this afternoon and we will get sunshine.

    A. cloudy   C. windy

    B. hot   D. wintery

14. **Overcast** skies are often associated with

    A. airplanes   C. radio

    B. birds   D. rain

15. **prolong**

Why are you **prolonging** this lesson? We have done enough for one day.

    A. lengthening   C. teaching

    B. studying   D. writing

16. When you **prolong** something, you

    A. avoid it   C. make it better

    B. drag it out   D. test it

17. **repetition**

I've heard that before. There is no need for the **repetition**.

    A. agreeing   C. saying again

    B. begging   D. shortness

18. The word **repetition** is derived from the word

    A. reap   C. pet

    B. repeat   D. petition

19. **tuition**

Public schools are free, but private schools charge **tuition**.

    A. the courses   C. the principal

    B. the fee a school   D. the school building
        charges

20. Who pays **tuition**?

    A. building staff   C. students

    B. graduates   D. teachers

D. Words with the Prefixes *Pro-* and *Trans-*

The prefix *pro-* means "earlier than" or "before," or "in front of," or "forward."

procession   [*noun*] Moving forward. In particular, a collection of people marching together or walking as a group. **Procession** comes from the verb **proceed**, from *pro-* plus a form of the Latin word meaning "to go."

proposition   [*noun*] Something **proposed**, that is, offered for discussion, usually in a formal way, as in a debate or as something to be voted on. From *pro-* plus a form of the Latin word meaning "to place."

provoke   [*verb*] To stir up an angry response. From **pro-** + a form of a Latin word meaning "to call." When you **provoke** you call forth anger.

The prefix **trans-** means "across" or "through" or "beyond."

transform   [*verb*] To change completely. From **trans-** + **form**. When you **transform** something, you change its form totally, from one end to the other.

transmit   [*verb*] To send. From **trans-** + a form of a Latin word meaning "to send." To **transmit** is to send from one place "across" to another.

(1–5) Choose the word or phrase with the **same** meaning, or almost the same meaning, as the word in bold type.

1. to **provoke** the crowd

    A. address   C. assure
    B. arouse   D. hide from

2. a stately **procession**

    A. dinner   C. marriage
    B. home   D. parade

3. to **transmit** the news

    A. anticipate   C. forward
    B. be saddened by   D. listen to

4. to **transform** his appearance

    A. criticize   C. help
    B. greatly alter   D. pay attention to

5. offer a **proposition**

    A. change   C. proof
    B. prayer   D. proposal

(6–8) Choose the word or phrase with the **opposite** meaning, or with the meaning which is most nearly opposite.

6. totally **transformed**

    A. deadened   C. unemotional
    B. the same   D. very inexpensive

7. **provoked** by what was said

    A. bored   C. caused to lose faith
    B. calmed down   D. informed

8. to **transmit** a signal

    A. blow up   C. not send
    B. fail to see   D. record

(9–10) Fill in the missing word in the sentence.

9. Are you going to march in the Easter
   _____?

    A. procession   C. transforming
    B. proposition   D. transmission

10. How are you going to vote on
    _____ in next Tuesday's
    election?

    A. Procession A   C. Transforming A
    B. Proposition A   D. Transmission A

95

E. Words with More than One Meaning

Each of the words in this lesson has at least two meanings, one when used as a noun and the other when used as a verb, and some have other meanings as well.

chime
    a. [*noun*] A device which makes a series of musical sounds, as with a doorbell or a clock striking the hour.

    b. [*verb*] To make such sounds. Also, in the expression **to chime in**, to show you agree.

flounder
    a. [*noun*] A round, flat ocean fish often used for food.

    b. [*verb*] To struggle to gain your footing, to move about clumsily.

function
    a. [*noun*] A big, formal ceremony.

    b. [*noun*] Something whose value depends on something else.

    c. [*noun*] A person's role or official position in something.

    d. [*noun*] Purpose.

    e. [*verb*] To be in action, to take part in.

mangle
    a. [*noun*] A machine used to press clothes.

    b. [*verb*] To beat an object to a point where it is very badly damaged.

relish
    a. [*verb*] To enjoy greatly.

    b. [*noun*] Delight in something.

    c. [*noun*] A mixture of such things as mustard, pickles, and catsup which you put on food to make it more flavorful.

(1–4) Choose the word or phrase with the **same** meaning, or almost the same meaning, as the word in bold type.

1. hear the **chimes**
   - A. bells
   - B. sales talk
   - C. screams
   - D. speeches

2. an important **function** in the story
   - A. moment
   - B. part
   - C. plot
   - D. science

3. **floundering** in math
   - A. doing poorly
   - B. repeating
   - C. studying hard
   - D. understanding

4. to **mangle** one's opponent
   - A. admire
   - B. beat on
   - C. conquer
   - D. flee from

(5) Choose the word or phrase with the **opposite** meaning, or with the meaning which is most nearly opposite.

5. to **relish** the thought of
   - A. dislike
   - B. fail to express
   - C. forget
   - D. remember as it was

96

(6) Pick out the best sentence to go with the definition.

6. A big formal ceremony

    A. Did you attend that big **function** in the library last Thursday evening?

    B. How much time it takes to drive there is a **function** of how bad the traffic is.

    C. What is her **function** in the organization?

(7–8) Answer the following questions.

7. A **mangle** is a machine used for

    A. jewelry   C. shirts
    B. pills   D. shoes

8. Where might you find a **flounder**?

    A. flying in the sky   C. on the dinner table
    B. in your shoe   D. under the bed

(9–10) Fill in the missing word in the sentence.

9. No wonder my brother got sick. Did you see how much _____ he put on his hamburger?

    A. chime   C. function
    B. flounder   D. relish

10. At first only a few of the students said they liked Janet's report. But then when the teacher said she liked it, they all _____ in.

    A. chimed   C. functioned
    B. floundered D. relished

F. Words with the Prefix *Re-*

The prefix *re-* comes from a Latin word with two somewhat different meanings, "again" and "back."

recruit   [*noun*] A person who has just joined an organization, particularly someone who has just joined the military. Also, [*verb*] to get people to join an organization. *Recruit* comes from *re-* + the Latin word for "grow." When you *recruit* for the army, you make it grow again.

refresh   [*verb*] To make fresh again.

relapse   [*verb*] To slip back into a former condition. From *re-* + a form of the Latin word for "slide." Also, [*noun*] the return of a sickness.

reproduce   a. [*verb*] To make a copy or to produce again.

             b. [*verb*] To give brith to offspring, often used in reference to animals, plants, germs, etc.

retain   [*verb*] To keep possession of. From *re-* + a form of the Latin word meaning "hold."

(1–2) Choose the word or phrase with the **same** meaning, or almost the same meaning, as the word in bold type.

1. when the dogs **reproduce**

   A. get fleas   C. have pups

   B. grow older   D. play

2. to **recruit** volunteers

   A. address   C. sign up

   B. lead   D. train

(3–6) Choose the word or phrase with the **opposite** meaning, or with the meaning which is most nearly opposite.

3. **have a relapse**

   A. become nervous   C. lose your eyesight

   B. get well   D. remember

4. to **retain** the services of

   A. cheat out of   C. let go of

   B. improve upon   D. not care about

5. feel **refreshed**

   A. anxious   C. sad

   B. pained   D. tired

6. army **recruit**

   A. battle victory   C. failure

   B. ex-soldier   D. permission

(7–8) Answer the following questions.

7. What do animals need to **reproduce**?

   A. exercise   C. mothers

   B. fur   D. warm weather

8. the prefix **re-** in **refresh** means

   A. about   C. back

   B. again   D. over

(9–10) Fill in the missing word in the sentence.

9. Harriet's mother seemed to be getting over her heart attack, but on Friday she had a _____.

   A. recruit   C. reproduce

   B. relapse   D. retain

10. I'm happy you were able to _____ most of your savings.

   A. recruit   C. relapse

   B. refresh   D. retain

G. Chapter 8 Review

(1–7) Choose the word or phrase with the **same** meaning, or almost the same meaning, as the word in bold type.

1. a **sterling** platter

   A. broken   C. tasty

   B. silver   D. wonderful

2. a **blotter** on the desk

   A. a hard surface   C. something used to soak up ink

   B. a pen and pencil set   D. telephone equipment

3. a real estate **investment**

   A. advice to buyers and sellers   C. money-making purchase

   B. book listing houses for sale   D. property

4. a salesperson's **persistence**

   A. cleverness   C. presentation

   B. earnings   D. refusing to give up

5. a *pawn* in the struggle
   - A. battle
   - B. prize
   - C. something that a competitor is willing to sacrifice
   - D. very important part

6. high *pollen* count
   - A. dust from flowers
   - B. level of sickness
   - C. measure of food value
   - D. number of voters

7. suffer a *relapse*
   - A. defeat
   - B. loss of consciousness
   - C. painful shoulder injury
   - D. return of a sickness

(8–12) Choose the word or phrase with the **opposite** meaning, or with the meaning which is most nearly opposite.

8. an *edible* fruit
   - A. bitter
   - B. fattening
   - C. poisonous
   - D. winter

9. an *infantile* remark
   - A. adult
   - B. complimentary
   - C. long-winded
   - D. understandable

10. the building's *exterior*
   - A. cost to construct
   - B. decorations
   - C. inside
   - D. permit to build

11. a place for the *excess*
   - A. future earnings
   - B. living matter
   - C. too small an amount
   - D. worthless possessions

12. decide whether or not there was *arson*
   - A. cooperation
   - B. putting out a fire
   - C. rebellion
   - D. use of safe medicines

(13–17) Fill in the missing word in the sentence.

13. The _____ at a private college is expensive.
   - A. clutter
   - B. finance
   - C. recruit
   - D. tuition

14. Put a little _____ in the water to help you get off that dirt and grime.
   - A. ammonia
   - B. asbestos
   - C. curfew
   - D. frolic

15. You should be able to solve that problem by using simple _____.
   - A. applicant
   - B. custody
   - C. defendant
   - D. logic

16. She is a(n) _____ Baptist.
   - A. devout
   - B. jovial
   - C. overcast
   - D. pastel

17. This little radio device can _____ messages as far away as China.
   - A. prolong
   - B. reproduce
   - C. retain
   - D. transmit

(18–19) Choose the word that has the two meanings that are in bold type.

18. *move about clumsily*; *ocean fish*
   - A. flounder
   - B. mackerel
   - C. reel
   - D. salmon

19. *delight in something*; *mixture you put on hamburgers*
   - A. relish
   - B. sauce
   - C. seasoning
   - D. zest

(20) Pick out the best sentence to go with the definition.

20. purpose

    A. How well you do in that course is a *function* of how hard you study.

    B. The graduation ceremony is an important *function*.

    C. What's the *function* of that little knob?

(21) Answer the following question.

21. What is the meaning of the prefix *pro-* in *provoke*?

    A. almost   C. forth

    B. by   D. in favor of

(22) Look carefully at the pair of words in capitals. Try to figure out the relationship between them. Then choose the sentence that does the **best** job of showing how the words are related.

22. BLOTTER : INK

    A. A blotter can be placed under a bottle of ink.

    B. A blotter is often the color of ink.

    C. A blotter is used to soak up ink.

(23–25) Figure out how the first two words in capitals are related to each other. Then choose the pair of words below it that are related in the same way.

23. BLOTTER : INK

    A. IN : OUT

    B. RED : BLUE

    C. SPONGE : WATER

24. EXTERIOR : INSIDE

    A. BUILDER : HOUSE

    B. FATHER : SON

    C. HEAD : TAILS

25. ARSON : FIRE

    A. MURDER : DEATH

    B. SUMMER : VACATION

    C. WAR : PEACE

CHAPTER 9.

Words in this chapter:

abolish
abbreviate
accelerate
accumulate
adjoin
adjourn
admittance

becalm
born
borne

census
clog
confer

deduct
dictate

eliminate
enrich
envelop

falter
flew
flue
fortify

gait
gate

ignite
inflate
intrigue

justify

mystify

nourish

pasteurize
pollute
probe
propel
prosperous

racial
regrettable
respectable
restrict

scaly
scorch
senses
shrivel
specify

tacked
tact
temporary

uphold
upholster

ventilate

A. Verbs with Simple Definitions

clog	to overload, to jam up
eliminate	to do away with
envelop	to surround, to enclose (Do *not* confuse with **envelope**, with an **e** on the end, which is a noun meaning "wrapper," particularly for letters.)
ignite	to set on fire
nourish	to feed, to support
pollute	to cause to be dirty or impure
restrict	to restrain, to keep within bounds
scorch	to burn the surface of
shrivel	to dry up and shrink
uphold	to give support to

(1–5) Choose the word or phrase with the **same** meaning, or almost the same meaning, as the word in bold type.

1. **clogged** with dirt

    A. covered
    B. filled up
    C. loaded on a truck
    D. made ugly

2. to **ignite** the stove

    A. cook meat over
    B. light a match to
    C. polish
    D. turn off

3. to **scorch** your shirt

    A. leave a burn mark on
    B. put in the washing machine
    C. sew on a button
    D. tear off a thread from

4. an **enveloping** storm

    A. cold and wet
    B. encircling
    C. passing
    D. thundering

5. to **uphold** an opinion

    A. back
    B. have
    C. oppose
    D. state

(6–10) Choose the word or phrase with the **opposite** meaning, or with the meaning which is most nearly opposite.

6. to **pollute** the stream

    A. change the course of
    B. clean up
    C. get out of
    D. pour water into

7. to **eliminate** several jobs

    A. add
    B. do all at once
    C. leave
    D. refuse

8. a **shriveled** old lady

    A. big and fat
    B. generous
    C. mean
    D. sane

9. to **nourish** the animals

    A. grow hair on
    B. sell
    C. starve
    D. turn loose

10. *restricted* movement

    A. backward   C. feeble

    B. exciting   D. free

(11–15) Fill in the missing word in the sentence.

11. This has been a _____ hot day.

    A. clogging   C. scorching

    B. polluting   D. shriveling

12. All men on the base have been _____ to their barracks.

    A. eliminated   C. restricted

    B. enveloped   D. upheld

13. A diet of potato chips and soda is not very _____.

    A. enveloping   C. nourishing

    B. igniting   D. upholding

14. The coach told his linebackers to _____ the middle to keep the fullback from gaining so many yards.

    A. clog   C. scorch

    B. envelop   D. shrivel

15. The ugly black smoke from that building _____ the air.

    A. ignites   C. pollutes

    B. nourishes   D. scorches

B. Verbs with Longer Definitions

becalm	For a sailboat, to lose the wind and be unable to move.
falter	To stumble, to lose your courage and act or speak weakly or with hesitation.
inflate	To put air into. Or more generally, to exaggerate or build up to an exaggerated size.
intrigue	To arouse interest. Also, as a *noun*, a tricky plot or scheme.
justify	To prove something was worthwhile, or to make something worthwhile.
mystify	To bewilder, to make something very hard to understand.
pasteurize	To heat a liquid, particularly milk, to the point where you get rid of its germs.
probe	To explore, to look into. Or, as a *noun*, a study, an investigation. Or a device for exploring some particular thing (as in surgery, space exploration, etc.).
specify	To list in detail, to make clear. Or to identify a choice exactly.
upholster	To cover a piece of furniture (such as a stuffed chair or a couch) with fabric.

(1–5) Choose the word or phrase with the **same** meaning, or almost the same meaning, as the word in bold type.

1. *pasteurized* milk

   A. germ-free   C. high in fat content
   B. guaranteed   D. with the cream
       fresh   mixed in

2. *upholstered* livingroom set

   A. covered   C. old
   B. expensive   D. wooden

3. to *probe* the bottom of the ocean

   A. bring up from   C. investigate
   B. fish in   D. sink to

4. to *specify* your reasons

   A. dramatize   C. repeat
   B. explain   D. think about

5. *faltering* speech

   A. clever   C. memorized
   B. halting   D. nasty

(6–10) Choose the word or phrase with the **opposite** meaning, or with the meaning which is most nearly opposite.

6. to *inflate* the tire

   A. put a patch on   C. take off the wheel
   B. stop using   D. take the air out of

7. a *becalmed* boat

   A. filled with pas-   C. moving swiftly
       sengers   through the water
   B. modern   D. repaired

8. to *intrigue* the audience

   A. bore   C. lose count of
   B. learn from   D. send away

9. to *justify* the cost

   A. add to   C. fail to explain
   B. erase   D. refuse to pay

10. a *mystifying* set of facts

   A. complex   C. understandable
   B. threatening   D. very small

(11–15) Fill in the missing word in the sentence.

11. I find your story so _____ I'd like to hear more of it.

   A. becalming   C. intriguing
   B. inflated   D. upholstered

12. When you fill out one of these forms, they always ask you to _____ details about your education.

   A. justify   C. probe
   B. mystify   D. specify

13. You can save a lot of money by _____ that couch yourself, but it's an awfully big job.

   A. inflating   C. probing
   B. pasteurizing   D. upholstering

14. Milk you buy from the farmer is very fresh, but it isn't _____.

   A. faltered   C. mystified
   B. inflated   D. pasteurized

15. You're supposed to _____ those bike tires to 70 pounds pressure.

   A. becalm   C. inflate
   B. falter   D. probe

C. Definitions for You to Derive from Context

Read the sentence following the word in bold type and on the basis of what you read, choose the correct definition.

1. **abolish**

   The principal has promised to **abolish** all rules having to do with the clothes you wear to school. You will be able to wear whatever you want.

   A. do away with   C. strengthen
   B. revise   D. write

2. opposite of **abolish**

   A. establish   C. make a final attempt
   B. leave   D. send

3. **admittance**

   She was refused **admittance**. They absolutely refused to let her inside.

   A. admission of guilt   C. freedom
   B. assistance   D. permission to enter

4. opposite of **admittance**

   A. freedom to leave   C. speed
   B. keeping to yourself   D. success

5. **enrich**

   Having a lot of hobbies **enriches** your life, not by making you richer in terms of money, but by making you healthier and happier.

   A. explores   C. lengthens
   B. improves   D. makes more expensive

6. How do food manufacturers **enrich** certain foods (such as cereals)?

   A. add vitamins and minerals   C. change names
   B. advertise   D. do a taste test

7. **propel**

   When you shoot off a rocket, you **propel** it into the air. When you bowl, you **propel** the bowling ball down the alley.

   A. check   C. pick up
   B. light   D. send off

8. The word **propel** has the idea of

   A. efficiency   C. roundness
   B. forward motion   D. skill

9. **prosperous**

   The families who live in the little houses at the bottom of the hill are poor, but the ones who live in the big houses at the top of the hill are **prosperous**.

   A. high up   C. sizable
   B. retired   D. well-off economically

10. Which of the following is likely to be the most **prosperous**?

    A. orphan   C. person who just joined the army
    B. owner of a business   D. student

11. **racial**

    Blacks, Whites, and Asians are the largest **racial** groups.

    A. based on race   C. numerous
    B. historical   D. scientific

12. Which of the following is often considered a **racial** characteristic?

    A. age   C. number of brothers and sisters
    B. grades in school   D. skin color

13. **regrettable**

    We're all sorry Dad wrecked the car. It's one of those **regrettable** things in life, but we will get over it.

    A. memorable   C. sudden
    B. peaceful   D. unfortunate

14. Something that is **regrettable** causes feelings of

    A. anger   C. jealousy
    B. helplessness   D. regret

15. **respectable**

Mom said my dress is too loud to wear on a job interview, but I think it's perfectly *respectable*.

A. decent   C. long lasting
B. fitted   D. stylish

16. Something that is *respectable* is worthy of

A. doing away with   C. respect
B. purchase   D. winning

17. **scaly**

When a sunburn begins to heal, your skin gets *scaly*.

A. bloody   C. diseased
B. creamy colored   D. flaky

18. What kind of animal tends to have *scaly* skin?

A. bird   C. fish
B. dog   D. worm

19. **temporary**

This is only a *temporary* job. I'll only be working here a few weeks.

A. endless   C. for a short time
B. evening   D. uncertain

20. opposite of *temporary*

A. laughable   C. skilled
B. permanent   D. substitute

D. Words Which Are Homophones

Homophones are words which sound alike but have different spellings and different meanings.

borne/born

borne   [*adjective*] Carried, supported. **Borne** comes from the verb to **bear**, which means "to carry."

born   [*adjective*] Given birth to, brought into existence.

census/
senses

census   [*noun*] A count of people or things. The government takes a **census** every 10 years of all the people in the country.

senses   (*noun*, plural) The basic ways of experiencing things and feeling things—sight, hearing, smell, taste, and touch. Or, more generally, feelings or awareness.

flue/flew

flue   [*noun*] The passageway in a chimney that lets the smoke and flames go up and out.

flew   [*verb*] Past tense of **fly**.

gait/gate

gait   [*noun*] One of the four different ways a horse walks or runs: walk, trot, pace, or canter. Also, the way a person walks: a slow **gait**, etc.

gate   [*noun*] Opening or doorway in a fence.

tact/tacked

tact   [*noun*] Good manners. Ability to say or do things that are polite and don't get people angry.

tacked   [*verb*] Past tense of *tack.*

(1–3) Choose the word or phrase with the **same** meaning, or almost the same meaning, as the word in bold type.

1. done with *tact*

   A. a hammer   C. politeness
   B. great effort   D. scorn

2. a complete *census*

   A. disaster   C. leveling off
   B. feeling   D. listing

3. *borne* into the air

   A. came out   C. started up
   B. lifted   D. swung around

(4–7) Answer the following questions.

4. Which of the following has *gaits*?

   A. pony   C. river
   B. ring   D. wall

5. When would you close a *flue*?

   A. when a bird is   C. when there is no
       building its nest   fire in the fireplace
   B. when a plane   D. when you are late
       takes off   for school

6. A *census* tells you

   A. how many   C. what you feel inside
   B. the distances   D. who the winner
       between cities   was

7. Troubles sometimes have to be *borne*. What does that mean?

   A. they have to be   C. they have to be
       done away with   reported
   B. they have to be   D. they have to be
       put up with   understood

(8–10) Fill in the missing word in the sentence.

8. You need good ears and eyes to have good _____.

   A. census   C. gate
   B. gait   D. senses

9. When a baby is _____, it rarely has hair on top of its head.

   A. born   C. tacked
   B. borne   D. tact

10. In the last _____, did they count all the people who own their own homes?

   A. census   C. gait
   B. flue   D. tact

E. Verbs with More than One Meaning

All the words in this lesson are verbs with more than one common meaning.

confer
    a. To grant (as, for example, "to *confer* a compliment upon someone").
    b. To consult, to compare ideas with someone.

deduct
    a. To subtract.
    b. To detract (used with *from*). To take attention away from.

dictate
    a. To issue a command, to be demanding.
    b. To speak "*dictation*," where what you say is written down by a secretary or recorded by a machine.

fortify
    a. To strengthen.
    b. To add minerals or vitamins to a food.

ventilate
    a. To bring in fresh air.
    b. To express openly.

(1–4) Choose the word or phrase with the **same** meaning, or almost the same meaning, as the word in bold type.

1. to **confer about** the new plans
    A. change   C. discuss
    B. design   D. put into effect

2. helps to **ventilate** the room
    A. air out   C. design
    B. decorate   D. empty out

3. **deducts from** its value
    A. computes   C. lowers
    B. improves   D. transfers

4. **dictate** the terms of peace
    A. accept   C. set forth
    B. observe   D. work out

(5–7) Choose the word or phrase with the **opposite** meaning, or with the meaning which is most nearly opposite.

5. amounts to be **deducted**
    A. added to   C. kept secret
    B. agreed to   D. minimized

6. to **fortify** their positions
    A. alter   C. flee from
    B. build higher   D. weaken

7. **confer** an honor
    A. feel sad about   C. pick out
    B. insist upon   D. take away

(8) Answer the following question.

8. Which of the following products is most likely to be **fortified**?
    A. cereal   C. newspaper
    B. leather gloves   D. television set

(9–10) Fill in the missing word in the sentence.

9. The purpose of this discussion session is to allow you to _____ your complaints.

   A. confer   C. dictate
   B. deduct   D. ventilate

10. Jennifer's mother is such a busy executive! She even _____ letters into a recording device while she is driving to work.

    A. confers   C. dictates
    B. deducts   D. ventilates

F. Verbs with the Prefix *Ad-*

The prefix *ad-* comes from a Latin word meaning "to" or "toward" or "together." It sometimes occurs in the forms *ab-*, *ac-*, and *ap-*, and in other forms as well, depending upon the first letter of the word to which it is attached.

abbreviate To shorten, particularly to shorten a name or word, such as "Fla." for "Florida," or "don't" for "do not."—From *ad-* + a form of the Latin word for "short."

accelerate To speed up. From *ad-* + a form of the Latin word for "swift." When you *accelerate*, you move more and more swiftly toward an object.

accumulate To collect, to gather a lot of things together. From *ad-* + a form of the Latin word meaning "to heap together."

adjoin To lie next to, to touch. Or to join together.

adjourn To end a meeting. From *ad-* + a form of a French wording meaning "day." When you *adjourn* a meeting, you come to the end of the meeting, which is often the end of the day's work.

(1–4) Choose the word or phrase with the **same** meaning, or almost the same meaning, as the word in bold type.

1. to *adjourn* the session

   A. address   C. halt
   B. attend   D. report on

2. an *abbreviated* version

   A. common   C. more intense
   B. made briefer D. slightly changed

3. *accelerated* payments

   A. costlier   C. more frequent
   B. in two parts D. sensible

4. to *accumulate* belongings

   A. move   C. sort through
   B. pile up D. store

(5–8) Choose the word or phrase with the **opposite** meaning, or with the meaning which is most nearly opposite.

5. *adjoining* rooms

   A. planned   C. similar
   B. separated D. uncomfortable

6. to *accelerate* the car

   A. acquire   C. start
   B. slow down D. straighten out

7. to *accumulate* over the years

   A. grow younger   C. see frequently

   B. lose   D. weaken

8. to *abbreviate* a name

   A. change   C. lengthen

   B. forget   D. repeat

(9–10) Fill in the missing word in the sentence.

9. The meeting has been _____ until noon tomorrow.

   A. abbreviated   C. adjourned

   B. adjoined   D. accelerated

10. Our farm _____ the state park on one side.

   A. abbreviates   C. adjoins

   B. accumulates   D. adjourns

G. Chapter 9 Review

(1–7) Choose the word or phrase with the **same** meaning, or almost the same meaning, as the word in bold type.

1. *polluting* the air

   A. adding poisons to   C. expanding

   B. breathing in   D. flying high in

2. a *nourishing* meal

   A. evening   C. healthy

   B. free   D. welcome

3. to *fortify* the town

   A. capture   C. see the sights in

   B. pass through   D. strengthen the defenses of

4. *shriveled* skin

   A. bruised   C. on the top of the head

   B. dried out   D. reddish

5. the *eliminated* teams in the tournament

   A. competing for the first time   C. knocked out

   B. favorite   D. selected

6. an *inflated* report

   A. complaining   C. frightening

   B. exaggerated   D. written out

7. a slow *gait*

   A. attendance   C. door

   B. creaking noise   D. walk or trot

(8–12) Choose the word or phrase with the **opposite** meaning, or with the meaning which is most nearly opposite.

8. situation requiring *tact*

   A. decrease in pay   C. retreat

   B. poor manners   D. show of strength

9. let us *adjourn*

   A. disagree   C. forget about it

   B. do whatever we can   D. start up the meeting

10. to *clog* the sink

   A. attach the pipes to   C. open up

   B. clean   D. take away from

11. a *prosperous* cousin

   A. distant   C. poor

   B. on the mother's side   D. younger

12. a **respectable** showing

    A. increasing   C. not permitted
    B. next   D. pretty lousy

(13–18) Fill in the missing word in the sentence.

13. Did you open the _____ in the fireplace?

    A. flew   C. tacked
    B. flue   D. tact

14. You can _____ the car when you are coming out of the curve.

    A. abolish   C. becalm
    B. accelerate   D. envelop

15. My boss _____ four long letters to me this morning.

    A. abbreviated   C. deducted
    B. accumulated   D. dictated

16. Most of the milk sold in this country is _____.

    A. justified   C. pasteurized
    B. mystified   D. scorched

17. I wonder how many people the 1990 _____ will show there are in Texas.

    A. census   C. restrict
    B. probe   D. senses

18. Where did your sister learn how to _____ chairs?

    A. adjoin   C. uphold
    B. enrich   D. upholster

(19–20) Choose the word that has the two meanings that are in bold type.

19. **to compare ideas**; **to give out**

    A. concede   C. consult
    B. confer   D. grant

20. **tricky scheme**; **arouse interest**

    A. entice   C. plot
    B. intrigue   D. swindle

(21) Answer the following question.

21. What does the prefix **ad-** in **adjoin** mean?

    A. away from   C. not
    B. extra   D. together

(22–25) Figure out how the first two words in capitals are related to each other. Then choose the pair of words below it that are related in the same way.

22. DEDUCT : ADD

    A. EAT : GROW
    B. PULL : PUSH
    C. READ : SING

23. FLUE : CHIMNEY

    A. GATE : FENCE
    B. GATE : LOCK
    C. GATE : OPEN

24. FISH : SCALY

    A. BEAR : FURRY
    B. BIRD : FEATHER
    C. DOG : BITE

25. UPHOLSTER : CHAIR

    A. CLOTHE : BODY
    B. MILK : COW
    C. WATER : PLANT

CHAPTER 10.

Words in this chapter:

adolescent
adrift
analysis
analyze
annex
antiseptic

budget

certification
certify
classic
classify
clause
clinic
convert
counterfeit

decompose
deflate
deprive
desolate
detain
divorce
drab

electrocute
electrocution
entitle

fiancé
fiancée
financial
floral

gospel
gross

heroic
hilarious

immortal
intermediate

jubilant

leaflet
liberal
lisp

masquerade
morale

quote

ruthless

sane
sanitation
scoff
serenade
spiritual
spry
sullen
surge
surplus
swerve
swindle

A. Adjectives with Simple Definitions

adrift	not tied down, drifting
drab	dull, uninteresting
financial	having to do with money
floral	having to do with flowers
heroic	very courageous
hilarious	very funny
jubilant	very, very happy
ruthless	terribly cruel, showing no mercy
sane	mentally healthy
spry	physically or mentally quick, usually with reference to an older person

(1–5) Choose the word or phrase with the **same** meaning, or almost the same meaning, as the word in bold type.

1. the *financial* section of the newspaper

    A. advertising   C. editorial
    B. business   D. news reporting

2. a *floral* arrangement

    A. desirable   C. generous
    B. difficult   D. made up of flowers

3. a *ruthless* general

    A. competent   C. ferocious
    B. decorated   D. weak

4. *adrift* in the sea

    A. at the bottom   C. growing
    B. floating around D. swimming

5. a *spry* old man

    A. active   C. demanding
    B. always thinking   D. sickly
       of the past

(6–10) Choose the word or phrase with the **opposite** meaning, or with the meaning which is most nearly opposite.

6. a *heroic* effort

    A. cowardly   C. final
    B. done on the   D. sincere
       spur of the
       moment

7. *drab* surroundings

    A. awful   C. exciting
    B. closed   D. modern

8. a *hilarious* story

    A. easy to   C. questionable
       understand
    B. overly long   D. solemn

9. a *jubilant* occasion

    A. early   C. playful
    B. easily forgotten D. sad

113

10. a *sane* person

   A. crazy   C. immature
   B. dependent   D. phony

(11–15) Fill in the missing word in the sentence.

11. Meg's new summer dress has a
_____ pattern with bunches of
roses and violets.

   A. drab   C. hilarious
   B. floral   D. jubilant

12. Andrew Porter is a _____ politician who has destroyed the careers of
many of the people he has dealt with and
who will do anything to win the election.

   A. drab   C. ruthless
   B. heroic   D. sane

13. You may think she's _____,
but so far as I can tell, she's talking utter
nonsense.

   A. adrift   C. sane
   B. financial   D. spry

14. The poor young man found himself
_____ in the world, not knowing where to go or what to do.

   A. adrift   C. sane
   B. hilarious   D. spry

15. Buying on credit is not going to solve your
_____ problems.

   A. drab   C. floral
   B. financial   D. jubilant

B. Words with Longer Definitions

adolescent   [*noun*] A young person who is physically maturing but has not yet reached adulthood. Also, [*adjective*] describing such a person.

analyze/
analysis   [*verb*] To **analyze** is to study a situation. To figure out how the parts fit together. The *noun* **analysis** comes from the *verb* to **analyze**. It refers to the end product of **analyzing**, the study itself, the figuring out of how the parts fit together.

certify/
certification   [*verb*] To **certify** is to guarantee that something is correct, usually to make a formal guarantee, often in writing. The *noun* **certification** refers to the guarantee itself.

classify   [*verb*] To **classify** is to arrange in groups. The result of **classifying** is a **classification** [*noun*].

electrocute/
electrocu-
tion   [*verb*] To **electrocute** is to kill by electric shock. The act of killing this way is called an **electrocution** [*noun*].

entitle　　　[*verb*] To give someone the right or privilege to do something. Or to receive such a right.

immortal　　[*adjective*] Living forever. Or so famous as never to be forgotten. Also, [*noun*] a person who lives forever or remains famous forever.

scoff　　　　[*verb*] To jeer at, to make fun of, to show how little use you have for something.

sullen　　　 [adjective] Showing anger by acting in a gloomy, silent way and refusing to take part in things.

swerve　　　[*verb*] To move in a crooked course, to change direction suddenly.

(1–5) Choose the word or phrase with the **same** meaning, or almost the same meaning, as the word in bold type.

1. an **adolescent's** concern

   A. cousin's　　　C. student's
   B. foreigner's　　D. teenager's

2. to **scoff at** the report

   A. begin revising　　C. pore over
   B. gloat over　　　　D. sneer at

3. to **entitle** you to buy two tickets

   A. beg　　　　C. qualify
   B. encourage　D. send

4. to **analyze** how it works

   A. be amazed at　　C. explain
   B. determine　　　 D. make a change in

5. to **classify** the collection of rocks

   A. to break up　　 C. to prepare for selling
   B. to look over　　D. to sort and identify

(6–9) Choose the word or phrase with the **opposite** meaning, or with the meaning which is most nearly opposite.

6. a **certified** Picasso painting

   A. fake　　　C. ordinary
   B. late　　　 D. sold

7. **immortal** words

   A. amusing　　　　C. misunderstood
   B. easily forgotten　D. unspoken

8. to **swerve** the car

   A. drive in a　　　C. stop
      straight line
   B. repair　　　　　D. unload

9. a **sullen** reply

   A. cheerful　　C. ridiculous
   B. meek　　　 D. unexpected

(10) Answer the following question.

10. Who is most likely to die from **electrocution**?

   A. convicted　　 C. person who
      murderer　　　　overeats
   B. patient on the　D. soldier at the front
      operating table

115

(11–15) Fill in the missing word in the sentence.

11. Ask them to _____ the check to make sure it won't bounce.
    A. analyze   C. classify
    B. certify   D. entitle

12. My great grandfather is 97 years old and in wonderful health. Maybe he's _____.
    A. adolescent   C. immortal
    B. electrocuted D. sullen

13. You may _____ at the way Linda boasts about what a good athlete she is, but I did see her run to catch the bus the other day.
    A. analyze   C. scoff
    B. certify   D. swerve

14. A lot of _____ get pimples.
    A. adolescents C. classifications
    B. analyses   D. immortals

15. Carmen is _____ to a few days off. She's been working steadily at this job since last April.
    A. certified   C. entitled
    B. classified   D. swerving

C. Definitions for You to Derive from Context

Many of the words in this lesson can be used either as nouns, as verbs, or as adjectives, with similar meanings in each case. The other words are all nouns only.

1. **annex**
   The United States **annexed** Texas in 1845. Texas has been an independent country for several years before that, but most of its people were happy for it to become a part of the United States.
   A. assisted   C. joined
   B. invaded   D. took over

2. What do you think a building **annex** is?
   A. a wing of the C. the builder
      building
   B. the boiler   D. the roof

3. **antiseptic**
   Rub on an **antiseptic** to make sure you don't get an infection.
   A. food   C. sandpaper
   B. germ killer D. soap

4. A house that has an **antiseptic** look to it is
   A. colorful   C. old-fashioned
   B. filled with   D. very clean
      furniture

5. **budget**
   In my **budget** I set aside $9 per week for transportation, $6 for entertainment, $25 for meals, and $3 for laundry.
   A. banking   C. salary
      arrangement
   B. plan for   D. sales prices
      spending
      money

6. How do you **budget** your time?
   A. figure what to C. set the alarm
      do with it
      in advance
   B. look at your   D. wait
      watch

116

7. **clinic**

When you think of a *clinic*, you usually think of a medical *clinic*. But there are other types of *clinics*, too. For example, a tennis pro might hold a tennis *clinic*, to show people how to improve their game.

A. park
B. place you go for help
C. sports arena
D. store

8. Which of the following is an example of a medical *clinic*?

A. discovery of penicillin
B. overdose of drugs
C. part of a hospital that treats cancer
D. the flu

9. **convert**

When you visit a foreign country, you will have to *convert* some of your dollars into the type of money used in the foreign country.

A. budget
B. change over
C. save
D. spend

10. A *convert* to a particular religion has been

A. made priest
B. thrown out
C. told to pray
D. won over

11. **counterfeit**

Watch out for *counterfeit* $20 bills. There are some floating around that look almost exactly like the real thing.

A. antique
B. made of plastic
C. phony
D. very rare

12. What kind of device is used to *counterfeit* money?

A. auto engine
B. hi fi
C. printing press
D. sewing machine

13. **divorce**

Jed's parents *divorced* each other several years ago. His father got remarried almost immediately.

A. ended a marriage
B. had children
C. took an oath
D. went to work

14. opposite of the noun *divorce*

A. clear evidence
B. joining together
C. poor diet
D. weakness

15. **surge**

Things that *surge* act like waves.

A. become very hot
B. lose control
C. separate from each other
D. swell and sweep forward

16. What do you think a *surge* in electricity is?

A. battery
B. circuit
C. connection
D. sudden increase in current

17. **surplus**

We already had plenty of light bulbs. The ones you bought are *surplus*.

A. copied
B. difficult to understand
C. extra
D. fine and costly

18. opposite of the noun *surplus*

A. generosity
B. not enough
C. sameness
D. strength

19. **swindle**

Those crooks use every trick in the book in *swindling* people out of their money.

A. charging
B. cheating
C. robbing at gunpoint
D. winning

20. What word in this lesson is most closely related to the noun *swindle*?

A. budget
B. convert
C. counterfeit
D. surplus

D. Words for You to Look Up in the Dictionary

(1–10) Unless you are sure you know the meaning of each of the words in bold type, look it up in the dictionary. Then choose the word with a similar meaning.

1. gave to my *fiancée*

   A. close relative   C. engaged woman
   B. employee   D. favorite person

2. according to *gospel*

   A. branch of science   C. newspaper article
   B. election result   D. religious truth

3. an *intermediate* position

   A. changing   C. middle
   B. hidden   D. solid

4. a *liberal* serving

   A. delicious   C. generous
   B. formal   D. respectful

5. a slight *lisp*

   A. break in the action   C. problem
   B. limp   D. slurred speech

6. a *masquerade* party

   A. college graduation   C. outdoor
   B. mask and costume   D. wedding

7. high *morale*

   A. electrical wire   C. positive feeling
   B. good behavior   D. tower

8. a *quote* from Shakespeare

   A. character   C. plot
   B. play   D. words to remember

9. the *sanitation* department

   A. garbage removal   C. income tax
   B. health and hospitals   D. welfare

10. *serenade* his loved one

    A. comfort   C. pursue
    B. go off on a honeymoon with   D. sing songs for

(11–12) Answer the following questions.

11. What is the difference between a *fiancé* and a *fiancée*?

    A. one is a man, the other a woman
    B. one is a noun, the other an adjective
    C. one is older than the other
    D. the second is an old word, rarely used

12. In American politics, the opponents of *liberals* most often call themselves

    A. communists   C. democrats
    B. conservatives   D. independents

(13–15) Answer the following questions.

13. Jennifer went to the _____ party dressed up as a rock star.

    A. fiancé   C. masquerade
    B. gospel   D. sanitation

14. People with _____ have a terrible time with the "s" and "z" sounds.

    A. intermediates   C. morales
    B. lisps   D. serenades

15. After our victory Tuesday over Poly Tech, the _____ of the team was very high.

    A. gospel   C. liberal
    B. intermediate   D. morale

E. Words with More than One Meaning

The words in this lesson are a mix of nouns, verbs, and adjectives—all of them with more than one meaning.

classic
    a. [*adjective*] "Classical," describing or like things in ancient Greece and Rome.

    b. [*adjective*] From the best period (not necessarily the period of ancient Rome and Greece). For example, certain makes of cars from the 1930's are called "*classic*" cars.

    c. [*adjective*] Of lasting value, as with a famous literary work.

    d. [*noun*] something that has one of the qualities described above.

clause
    a. [*noun*] A section of a contract.

    b. [*noun*] In grammar, one of the main parts of a compound or complex sentence, that is, a sentence where the main parts are joined together by a conjunction (such as "and," "but," "or," "because," "after," "if," etc.)

gross
    a. [*adjective*] Very big or fat, to the point of being ugly.

    b. [*adjective*] Total, out-and-out.

    c. [*adjective*] Coarse and rude.

    d. [*noun*] A total of 12 dozen (144) things.

    e. [*verb*] To earn the total amount (before deductions or expenses) in pay or in a business deal.

leaflet
    a. [*noun*] A small leaf.

    b. [*noun*] A short printed flyer or booklet.

spiritual
    a. [*adjective*] Having to do with sacred matters.

    b. [*adjective*] Having to do with such things as ghosts and the spirit world.

    c. [*noun*] A religious song, particularly from the American South.

(1–2) Choose the word or phrase with the **same** meaning, or almost the same meaning, as the word in bold type.

1. hand out a *leaflet*

    A. parking ticket   C. reward
    B. printed sheet   D. warning

2. *gross* thing to say

    A. familiar   C. polite
    B. pointed   D. vulgar

119

(3–4) Choose the word or phrase with the **opposite** meaning, or with the meaning which is most nearly opposite.

3. *spiritual* experience

    A. fresh   C. trying
    B. hopeful   D. worldly

4. a book that is considered a *classic*

    A. adult   C. of little value
    B. exciting   D. old-fashioned

(5–6) Fill in the missing word in the sentence.

5. Where do you learn about *clauses*?

    A. English   C. math
    B. health education D. science

6. Which date is found in *classic* Greek times?

    A. 70,000 B.C.   C. 1932
    B. 400 B.C.   D. 1987

(7–8) Pick out the best sentence to go with the definition.

7. 12 dozen

    A. How much is your *gross* pay?
    B. My company bought a *gross* of light bulbs
    C. That is a *gross* error.

8. religious song(s)

    A. Do you believe in the *spiritual* world of goblins and elves?
    B. Mother has an old book of *spirituals*.
    C. You should pay more attention to *spiritual* matters.

(9–10) Fill in the missing word in the sentence.

9. Did you see "Casablanca" on TV last night? it's one of the all-time _____.

    A. classics   C. leaflets
    B. clauses   D. spirituals

10. We spent a whole hour in science class studying a single tiny _____ from a tree.

    A. clause   C. leaflet
    B. gross   D. spiritual

F. Words with the Prefix *De-*

The prefix *de-* can mean "from," "down from," or "away from." In front of verbs, it can mean "do the opposite of" or "remove from."

decompose [*verb*] To rot, to decay. From *de-* + *compose*, meaning "to create," "to put together." In this case, *de-* means "do the opposite of."

deflate [*verb*] To take the air out of, to make smaller or less important. From *de-* + a form of the Latin word meaning "to blow."

deprive [*verb*] To hold back something or to take something away. From *de-* + a form of the Latin word meaning "to take away."

desolate [*adjective*] Deserted, lonely, gloomy. From *de-* + a form of the Latin word for "alone." Something that is *desolate* is alone, away from everything.

detain [*verb*] To hold someone back. From *de-* + a form of the Latin word meaning "to hold."

(1–2) Choose the word or phrase with the **same** meaning, or almost the same meaning, as the word in bold type.

1. a **desolate** island

   A. hot
   B. lifeless
   C. mountainous
   D. river

2. **deprived** childhood

   A. fondly remem-
      bered
   B. loving
   C. neglected
   D. unexciting

(3–7) Choose the word or phrase with the **opposite** meaning, or with the meaning which is most nearly opposite.

3. a **desolate** feeling

   A. happy
   B. sick
   C. strange
   D. wide-awake

4. **detained** for a few minutes

   A. amused
   B. let go
   C. made to feel
      uncomfortable
   D. questioned

5. begun to **decompose**

   A. be preserved
   B. rise up
   C. suffer
   D. yield

6. to **deflate** the raft

   A. blow up
   B. fix up
   C. turn right side up
   D. untie

7. to **deprive** you of your victory

   A. envy
   B. give
   C. insure
   D. not tell

(8–10) Fill in the missing word in the sentence.

8. I don't want to ＿＿＿＿＿＿＿ you of your lunch hour.

   A. decompose
   B. deflate
   C. deprive
   D. detain

9. The garbage will ＿＿＿＿＿＿＿.

   A. decompose
   B. deprive
   C. deflate
   D. detain

10. To change the tire on your bike, you will first have to ＿＿＿＿＿＿＿ the tube.

    A. decompose
    B. deflate
    C. deprive
    D. detain

G. Chapter 10 Review

(1–7) Choose the word or phrase with the **same** meaning, or almost the same meaning, as the word in bold type.

1. **decomposing** flesh

   A. fat
   B. frying
   C. rotting
   D. tasty

2. never seen people more **jubilant**

   A. happy
   B. in agreement
   C. tired
   D. troubled

3. your **immortal** soul

   A. deep
   B. everlasting
   C. gentle
   D. sinful

4. be careful or you will be *electrocuted*
   - A. bawled out
   - B. chased out of town
   - C. elected to public office
   - D. killed by electric shock

5. a *hilarious* story
   - A. mournful
   - B. often repeated
   - C. very funny
   - D. with a happy ending

6. a *sullen* young lady
   - A. bitter
   - B. disappointing
   - C. unintelligent
   - D. violent

7. determine whether or not he is *sane*
   - A. faultless
   - B. mentally healthy
   - C. properly registered
   - D. worthy

(8–12) Choose the word or phrase with the **opposite** meaning, or with the meaning which is most nearly opposite.

8. *adrift* in a boat
   - A. anchored
   - B. moving swiftly
   - C. rocking back and forth
   - D. sinking

9. a *liberal* teacher
   - A. dull
   - B. educated
   - C. male
   - D. strict

10. a *ruthless* enemy
    - A. defeated
    - B. merciful
    - C. not angry
    - D. smart

11. an *antiseptic* cream
    - A. approved
    - B. colorless
    - C. filled with germs
    - D. high in fat

12. go to the *annex*
    - A. beginning
    - B. lower level
    - C. main building
    - D. outside

(13–17) Fill in the missing word in the sentence.

13. My brother and his _____ are planning their wedding for early June.
    - A. adolescent
    - B. convert
    - C. divorce
    - D. fiancée

14. Meredith can't make it. She has an appointment at the eye _____ at the hospital to have her eyes checked.
    - A. clinic
    - B. counterfeit
    - C. sanitation
    - D. surplus

15. A school has to meet certain standards to be _____ by the state.
    - A. analyzed
    - B. certified
    - C. classified
    - D. entitled

16. Karen Ann can sing almost any kind of song—rock, _____, jazz—you name it.
    - A. floral
    - B. gospel
    - C. heroic
    - D. leaflet

17. My grandmother is still pretty _____ for someone her age. She even likes to go mountain climbing.
    - A. desolate
    - B. intermediate
    - C. spry
    - D. swindled

(18–19) Choose the word that has the two meanings that are in bold type.

18. *ancient Greek or Roman*; *famous literary work*
    - A. classic
    - B. classical
    - C. masterpiece
    - D. traditional

19. *section of a contract*; *section of a compound or complex sentence*
    - A. article
    - B. clause
    - C. conjunction
    - D. terms

(20) Pick out the best sentence to go with the definition.

20. ugly

    A. I think she's **gross**.
    B. My **gross** pay was about $300 last week.
    C. Order a **gross** of pencils.

(21) Answer the following question.

21. What does the prefix **de-** in **deprive** mean?

    A. from   C. together
    B. never   D. toward

(22–25) Figure out how the first two words in capitals are related to each other. Then choose the pair of words below it that are related in the same way.

22. BUDGET : MONEY

    A. DIET : FOOD
    B. LESSON : TEACHER
    C. SCORE : END

23. FUNNY : HILARIOUS

    A. ANGRY : FURIOUS
    B. ANGRY : IRRITATED
    C. ANGRY : SAD

24. SANE : CRAZY

    A. FAST : QUICK
    B. HAPPY : HAPPIER
    C. HONEST : DISHONEST

25. VICTORY : JUBILANT

    A. DEFEAT : SAD
    B. PLAN : RESULT
    C. SUCCESS : REWARD

CHAPTER 11.

Words in this chapter:

abnormal
application

base
beverage
binoculars

charter
coefficient
comedian
confetti
coupe

decoy
diploma
dissatisfied
doubtless

emigrate
encircle
endanger
endorse
enrollment
entangle
equation
escalator
exponent
expression
extension
extraordinary

factor
flannel

inequality
infuriate
isolate

lavatory
literary
lunatic

mortgage

nomad

pacify
pantomime
pharmacy
plaid
prior
product

quotient

security
skyscraper
surgeon

tragedy

variable
vaudeville
via

A. Nouns with Simple Definitions

beverage	drink
coupe	a two-door automobile
escalator	moving stairway
flannel	a soft woolen cloth
lavatory	a room with toilets and wash basins
lunatic	a crazy person
mortgage	a loan made on a building or property
pharmacy	drugstore
skyscraper	very tall building
surgeon	a doctor who specializes in doing operations

(1–5) Choose the word or phrase with the **same** meaning, or almost the same meaning, as the word in bold type.

1. a dangerous *lunatic*

   A. criminal   C. madman
   B. killer   D. opponent

2. bought a new *coupe*

   A. car   C. house
   B. dress   D. TV

3. choice of *beverage*

   A. dessert   C. main dish
   B. liquid refresh-   D. vegetable
       ment

4. a gray *flannel*

   A. color   C. plastic
   B. fabric   D. sky

5. works in a *skyscraper*

   A. factory   C. office tower
   B. farm   D. store

(6–10) Answer the following questions.

6. What might you buy in a *pharmacy*?

   A. aspirin   C. garden tools
   B. car battery   D. sports jacket

7. Where do *escalators* run?

   A. between floors   C. on the street
   B. in the ocean   D. up in the sky

8. What might a *surgeon* do?

   A. clean teeth   C. remove tonsils
   B. cut hair   D. score exams

9. Where are you likely to get a *mortgage*?

   A. bank   C. discount store
   B. city hall   D. movie theater

10. What are you likely to find in a *lavatory*?

    A. cat food   C. rocket engines
    B. paint brushes   D. soap and towels

(11–15) Fill in the missing word in the sentence.

11. My doctor referred me to a(n) _____.

    A. couple   C. lunatic
    B. escalator   D. surgeon

12. Do you prefer a(n) _____, or do you think you want a car with four doors?

    A. coupe   C. lunatic
    B. escalator   D. surgeon

13. Melanie's new suit is made of a brown _____ with black stripes.

    A. beverage   C. mortgage
    B. flannel   D. skyscraper

14. The seller of the house offered to give me a 12-year _____.

    A. beverage   C. mortgage
    B. flannel   D. skyscraper

15. Salvador is a druggist in the _____ down on Main Street.

    A. coupe   C. pharmacy
    B. lavatory   D. surgeon

B. Nouns with Longer Definitions

binoculars   Field glasses, for making things at a distance look bigger. Binoculars have two eyepieces, in contrast to a telescope, which has only one.

comedian   A funny person, particularly a performer who tells jokes or does funny things.

confetti   Small bits of paper thrown out of windows at parades or thrown at the bride and groom at weddings.

decoy   Something used to lead an animal or a person into a trap. For example, painted wooden birds are used as *decoys* to attract birds within the shooting range of a hunter.

diploma   The document you are given to show you have graduated from a particular school.

nomad   A wandering person. In particular, a member of a people with a way of life which involves wandering from place to place.

pantomime   Telling a story by body and facial movements, without words. Also, a play or performance acted in *pantomime*, that is, without dialogue or speech.

plaid   A pattern made by crossing stripes of different colors and widths. There are many *plaid* patterns. Most of them come from Scotland and are used on materials for dresses, scarves, and the like.

tragedy   Great misfortune. Also, a type of theatrical play which has a sad ending.

vaudeville   A stage show with a series of singing, dancing, and comedy acts. In the old days, movie houses often had *vaudeville* shows to go along with the movies.

(1–5) Choose the word or phrase with the **same** meaning, or almost the same meaning, as the word in bold type.

1. a type of **comedian**

   A. beauty queen   C. director
   B. clown   D. singer

2. the life of a **nomad**

   A. a person who roams around   C. a taxi driver
   B. a student   D. a worthless criminal

3. resulted in a **tragedy**

   A. an amusing scene   C. disaster
   B. an increase in price   D. something you could not have expected

4. a bright **plaid**

   A. checkered design   C. morning sun
   B. color   D. young person

5. used a **decoy**

   A. type of money   C. winter coat
   B. weapon   D. wooden duck

(6–10) Answer the following questions.

6. You get a **diploma** when you

   A. enter college   C. join the army
   B. finish high school   D. return from summer vacation

7. What is one use of **binoculars**?

   A. cooking   C. keeping afloat in water
   B. helping with the dishes   D. looking at birds

8. What do the bride and groom do with **confetti**?

   A. brush it off   C. sign it
   B. burn it   D. turn it in for money

9. A **pantomime** artist is skilled in

   A. hand movements   C. speech
   B. singing   D. wrestling

10. The purpose of **vaudeville** was

    A. to build strength   C. to entertain
    B. to educate   D. to help people find jobs

(11–15) Fill in the missing word in the sentence.

11. He was a singer in the old _____ shows.

    A. confetti   C. tragedy
    B. pantomime   D. vaudeville

12. The Indian tribes who hunted buffalo were usually _____.

    A. comedians   C. nomads
    B. decoys   D. plaids

13. This set of _____ is powerful enough to let you read the small print on that sign way across the road.

    A. binoculars   C. diplomas
    B. decoys   D. plaids

14. My mother always makes it sound like such a _____ when I don't get up on time.

    A. diploma   C. tragedy
    B. pantomime   D. vaudeville

15. Jack and I were standing outside the church waiting to throw _____, but the bride and groom went out the side door.

    A. confetti   C. tragedy
    B. plaids   D. vaudeville

C. Definitions for You to Derive from Context

Read the sentence following the word in bold type and on the basis of what you read, choose the correct definition.

1. **abnormal**
   There is nothing **abnormal** about our dog except that she has five legs.

   A. dangerous   C. valuable
   B. unusually large   D. very irregular

2. The prefix **ab-** in **abnormal** means

   A. away from   C. very
   B. for   D. within

3. **dissatisfied**
   If for any reason you are **dissatisfied** with the book, simply return it, and we will give you your money back.

   A. attempting to read   C. interested
   B. educated   D. not satisfied

4. opposite of **dissatisfied**

   A. content   C. fat
   B. energetic   D. learned

5. **doubtless**
   Alonzo's story was **doubtless** funny and interesting. He always writes amusing, wonderful stories.

   A. certainly   C. unfortunately
   B. possibly   D. within limits

6. The suffix **-less** in **doubtless** means

   A. again   C. to
   B. by   D. without

7. **emigrate**
   There was a terrible famine in Ireland. Thousands upon thousands of Irish men and women were forced to **emigrate** from their homeland and move to the United States.

   A. demand better pay   C. leave your country
   B. improve yourself   D. revolt

8. In the word **emigrate**, the stem **migrate** means "to travel." What does the prefix **e-** mean?

   A. former   C. not
   B. from   D. toward

9. **extraordinary**
   That was one of the best basketball games I have ever seen. It was really exceptional, truly **extraordinary**.

   A. easy   C. opposite
   B. frightening   D. remarkable

10. **Extraordinary** consists of two words. What are they?

    A. *ex* and *traordinary*   C. *extraor* and *dinary*
    B. *extra* and *ordinary*   D. *extraordin* and *ary*

11. **infuriate**

A comment like that *infuriates* me. I get so mad I can't see straight.

A. arouses interest in
B. informs
C. makes someone very angry
D. restrains

12. *Infuriate* is derived from the word

A. fry
B. fur
C. fury
D. infer

13. **isolate**

It is OK to go walking in the woods all by yourself if you don't mind being *isolated*, but I prefer to spend my time with other people.

A. alone
B. attacked
C. sunburned
D. tired

14. If you *isolate* a particular part of a problem, you

A. make sure it gets equal treatment
B. pay no attention to it
C. rescue it
D. separate it out from other parts

15. **literary**

Among the people there were artists from the art world, musicians from the world of music, and writers and publishers from the *literary* world.

A. assembled
B. having to do with books and writing
C. teaching
D. truthful

16. *Literary* people are for the most part

A. foreign citizens
B. learned
C. not yet 13 years old
D. very athletic

17. **prior**

I have the April bill. I would like you to send me a copy of the *prior* bill, the one from March.

A. combination
B. earlier
C. incorrect
D. unpaid

18. opposite of *prior*

A. cuter
B. later
C. major
D. open

19. **via**

We went from Texas to California *via* the Rocky Mountains and Salt Lake City.

A. because of
B. by way of
C. in the hope of
D. in the opposite direction of

20. *Via* comes from a Latin word. Can you guess its Latin meaning?

A. food or water
B. man or woman
C. road or path
D. sky or ocean

D. Words Used in Mathematics

Some of the following words have other meanings besides the ones in mathematics. But in this lesson, we are only interested in their math usage. A knowledge of many of these words will be particularly helpful when you begin to study algebra. All of these words are nouns.

coefficient In alegbra, we often use letters in place of numbers. A number *in front of* such a letter is called a *coefficient*. For example, in the term $7x$, 7 is the *coefficient*.

equation Another word in alegbra. An **equation** is a statement that two quantities are equal, that the left side is equal to the right side. For example:

$$9 + 24 = 33 \quad \textbf{\textit{or}}$$
$$3x = 9 \quad \textbf{\textit{or}}$$
$$a + b + c = 45p$$

All of the above are **equations**.

exponent/ When we write 2^3, the small 3 to the right and above is called the **exponent**. It
base tells you to mulitply 2 (the **base**) times itself 3 times (that is, $2 \times 2 \times 2$). Likewise, when we write x^5 the **base** is x and the **exponent** is 5, which tells you to mulitply x times itself 5 times.

expression A group of numbers and letter, such as:

$$16b \quad \textbf{\textit{or}}$$
$$3a + 7y + 2 \quad \textbf{\textit{or}}$$
$$x^5 + 9$$

All of the above are **expressions**.

factor In math, a number that you can multiply by another number to give a particular product. For example, 5 and 3 are **factors** which when multiplied by each other give 15. We call them **factors** of 15. Question: What are **factors** of 12? 4 times 3 equals 12, so 4 and 3 are **factors** of 12. So are 6 and 2.

inequality In math, the statement that the left side is *not* equal to the right side (as in an **equation**, see above). Mathematicians use many symbols to describe **inequalities**. For example: $8 + 4 < 20$ means "$8 + 4$ is less than 20"—an **inequality**.

product The result of a multiplication problem: $9 \times 2 = 18$; 18 is the **product**.

quotient The result of a division problem: $8 \div 2 = 4$; 4 is the **quotient**.

variable In math, a letter used in place of a number. For example, in the expression $7a + 3b$, a and b are **variables**. In $6xyz$, x, y, and z are **variables**. The reason they are called **variables** (from **to vary**, "to change") is that you can assign different numbers to them. You are not always tied down to the same numbers.

(1–10) Answer the following questions.

1. In the expression $7x + y + 9$, which number or letter is a **coefficient**?

   A. 7   C. y
   B. x D. 9

2. Which of the following is an **equation**?

   A. $5 + 3$ C. $a + 9$
   B. 7^2 D. $3 + x = 15$

3. In the term $4ab^2$, what is the **exponent**?

   A. 4   C. b
   B. a D. ^{2}

4. In the term 9^3, what is the **base**?

   A. 9   B. ^{3}

5. We know that $5 \times 4 = 20$. The 5 and the 4 are known as

   A. coefficients of 20   C. factors of 20
   B. equations of 20   D. products of 20

6. What is the **product** of 6×2?

   A. 6   C. 3
   B. 2   D. 12

7. What is the **quotient** of 15 divided by 5?

   A. 15   C. 3
   B. 5   D. 75

8. $a + 3x + 49$ is called

   A. a coefficient   C. an exponent
   B. an equation   D. an expression

9. Which of the following is an *inequality*?

   A. 13 + 5   C. 13 + 5 = *a*
   B. 13 + 5 = 18   D. 13 + 5 < 20

10. In the expression $4 + 3a + 19$, there is only one *variable*. What is it?

   A. 4   C. *a*
   B. 3*a*   D. 19

E. Words with More than One Meaning

Some of the words in this lesson are nouns. Others are verbs. All of them have more than one meaning.

application
   a. [*noun*] A request such as a request for a job.
   b. [*noun*] The form you use in applying for a job, or for something else.
   c. [*noun*] Strong effort.
   d. [*noun*] The use something can be put to.
   e. [*noun*] A bandage or medicine you put over a sore or other skin problem.

charter
   a. [*verb*] To rent an entire airplane, boat, or bus for the use of a particular group.
   b. [*verb*] To issue the basic contract which sets forth the rights of a particular group.
   c. [*noun*] The contract which sets forth these rights.

extension
   a. [*noun*] A part you can add on to something to lengthen it.
   b. [*noun*] A second telephone.
   c. [*noun*] Stretching out your body.
   d. [*noun*] In general, any lengthening.

pacify
   a. [*verb*] To calm down someone's anger.
   b. [*verb*] To conquer a country or an area or to subdue a revolt.

security
   a. [*noun*] Safety, protection.
   b. [*noun*] Property you agree a lender may take if you don't pay back a loan.

(1–2) Choose the word or phrase with the **same** meaning, or almost the same meaning, as the word in bold type.

1. put on an *extension*

   A. addition   C. covering
   B. assistant   D. decoration

2. *charter* a bus

   A. board   C. lease
   B. drive   D. wreck

(3–5) Choose the word or phrase with the **opposite** meaning, or with the meaning which is most nearly opposite.

3. help to *pacify*

   A. drop
   B. plant seed
   C. receive payment for a loan
   D. stir up trouble

4. a sense of *security*

   A. danger
   B. excitement
   C. hope
   D. ugliness

5. *application* of all her strength

   A. attacking with
   B. giving in to
   C. renewal
   D. weak use

(6–7) Pick out the best sentence to go with the definition.

6. second telephone

   A. Mom gave me an *extension* in my bedroom for my birthday.
   B. The bank offered us an *extension* on the loan.
   C. To reach the roof, you'll have to use the *extension* on the ladder.

7. request

   A. The *application* for planning board approval has been denied.
   B. The doctor put a healing *application* over the wound.
   C. What *application* does the math you're teaching us have?

(8) Answer the following question.

8. Who would be most likely to *pacify* a country?

   A. flier
   B. general
   C. salesperson
   D. scientist

(9–10) Fill in the missing word in the sentence.

9. They taught us how to fill out job
   _____.

   A. applications
   B. charters
   C. extensions
   D. securities

10. The bank wants us to use our house as _____ for the loan.

   A. application
   B. charter
   C. extension
   D. security

F. Words with the Prefix *En-*

The prefix *en-* has the basic meaning "cause to be" or "provide with" or to "go into or onto." It is usually found in front of verbs or in front of words formed from such verbs.

encircle   [*verb*] To surround. When you *encircle* something, you make a circle around it, that is, you "cause the circle to be."

endanger   [*verb*] to expose to danger. To cause to be dangerous.

endorse
   a. [*verb*] To sign your name to the back of a check. ***Endorse*** comes from ***en-*** + a form of the Latin word meaning "back." When you ***endorse*** a check, you cause your name to appear on the back.

   b. [*verb*] To express approval, to approve. When you ***endorse*** someone or something, it is just like signing your name to the back of a check.

enrollment (or enrolment)
   [*noun*] Joining up. Or the total number of people who have joined up ("***enrolled***") in a school or in a special program or the like.—From the verb ***enroll***, which comes from ***en-*** + a form of a French word meaning "to register." When you ***enroll*** in a school, you register yourself into it.

entangle
   [*verb*] To confuse, to complicate, or to get deeply involved in something. From ***en-*** + ***tangle***.

(1–3) Choose the word or phrase with the **same** meaning, or almost the same meaning, as the word in bold type.

1. the college's ***enrollment***

   A. course offerings   C. reputation
   B. fees   D. student body

2. ***encircling*** the camp

   A. enclosing   C. part of
   B. invading   D. starting from

3. ***entangled in*** a messy situation

   A. angered by   C. hurt by
   B. free from   D. mixed up in

(4–6) Choose the word or phrase with the **opposite** meaning, or with the meaning which is most nearly opposite.

4. to ***endorse*** his candidacy

   A. announce   C. reject
   B. gain from   D. work for

5. completely ***entangled***

   A. healthy   C. simplified
   B. pleasing   D. smart

6. an ***endangered*** species

   A. greedy   C. safe
   B. legal   D. vigorous

(7–8) Answer the following questions.

7. Which of the following has an ***enrollment***?

   A. University of   C. the Ford Motor
      Michigan   Company
   B. Houston, Texas   D. the NBC Television
                      Network

8. When you ***endorse*** a contract, what do you do?

   A. change it   C. put it away
   B. disregard it   D. write your name

(9–10) Fill in the missing word in the sentence.

9. Don't let Joey drive home. He's been drink-ing, and he'll _____ his own life and the lives of everyone in the car.

    A. encircle   C. endorse

    B. endanger   D. entangle

10. Do you _____ the Senator's plan for cleaning up the environment?

    A. encircle   C. endorse

    B. endanger   D. entangle

G. Chapter 11 Review

(1–7) Choose the word or phrase with the **same** meaning, or almost the same meaning, as the word in bold type.

1. a **vaudeville** show

    A. night club   C. television

    B. stage   D. trade

2. pay the **mortgage**

    A. house loan   C. state tax

    B. penalty   D. tuition

3. clean the **lavatory**

    A. attic   C. kitchen

    B. floor   D. washroom

4. throw out **confetti**

    A. bits of paper   C. leaves and grass

    B. bottles and cans   D. old clothes

5. available at the **pharmacy**

    A. airline   C. government office

    B. drugstore   D. vegetable stand

6. studying to be a **surgeon**

    A. doctor who does operations   C. language specialist

    B. flight engineer   D. trial lawyer

7. **endorse** it on the back

    A. grease   C. sign

    B. rub   D. turn over

(8–12) Choose the word or phrase with the **opposite** meaning, or with the meaning which is most nearly opposite.

8. **doubtless** true

    A. lovingly   C. singly

    B. questionably   D. sweetly

9. acting like a **lunatic**

    A. brilliant person   C. sane person

    B. dangerous per-son   D. shy person

10. an **isolated** example

    A. convincing   C. inappropriate

    B. far-fetched   D. one of many

11. **extraordinary** luck

    A. everyday   C. unique

    B. unexpected   D. unlikely

12. result in a **tragedy**

    A. cheap affair   C. happy event

    B. dull ending   D. wise decision

(13–15) Answer the following questions.

13. When we write 5^3, the small 3 is called the
    A. base   C. exponent
    B. coefficient   D. factor

14. In the expression $3x + 4y$, x and y are
    A. equations   C. quotients
    B. inequalities   D. variables

15. The prefix *en-* in *entangle*
    A. cause to be   C. into
    B. formerly   D. outside of

(16–18) Fill in the missing word in the sentence.

16. It is _____ to have 11 fingers and 14 toes.
    A. abnormal   C. infuriating
    B. encircling   D. literary

17. My mother is making me a dress from a beautiful woolen material with a _____ pattern.
    A. decoy   C. flannel
    B. diploma   D. plaid

18. The story was told completely in _____, without any words at all.
    A. beverage   C. pantomime
    B. extension   D. security

(19–20) Choose the word that has the two meanings that are in bold type.

19. *conquer a country*; *calm down someone's anger*
    A. appease   C. subdue
    B. pacify   D. vanquish

20. *second telephone*; *extending out your body*
    A. elongation   C. intercom
    B. extension   D. stretch

(21) Pick out the best sentence to go with the definition.

21. form you use to apply for a job
    A. Did you put an *application* of burn medicine on the burn?
    B. Have you filled out the *application*?
    C. What is the practical *application* of your discovery?

(22–25) Figure out how the first two words in capitals are related to each other. Then choose the pair of words below it that are related in the same way.

22. SKYSCRAPER : SKY
    A. FIELD : HAY
    B. ROAD : FOREST
    C. TUNNEL : GROUND

23. PRIOR : LATER
    A. FAT : FUNNY
    B. WHEN : WHERE
    C. WINNER : LOSER

24. COUPE : DOORS
    A. BOAT : MOTOR
    B. GUN : BULLETS
    C. MAN : LEGS

25. TEA : BEVERAGE
    A. CHEESE : MEAT
    B. PEPPER : SPICE
    C. VEGETABLE : SAUCE

LIST AND LOCATION
OF WORDS TAUGHT

List and Location of Words Taught
(numbers refer to chapters in the book)

external *2*
extinct *2*
extract *3*
extraordinary *11*

F
factor *11*
faculty *3*
falter *9*
faulty *2*
fiancé *10*
fiancée *10*
fidget *5*
finances *8*
financial *10*
fixture *3*
flannel *11*
flew *9*
flexible *2*
flinch *5*
floral *10*
flounder *8*
flue *9*
fore *6*
forestry *7*
foretell *5*
forgery *7*
fortify *9*
fossil *2*
frill *3*
frolic *8*
function *8*
furlough *6*

G
gadget *1*
gait *9*
garlic *4*
gate *9*
gill *7*
gospel *10*
graft *7*
gross *10*

H
habitation *4*
hazard *6*
heredity *2*
heroic *10*

hilarious *10*
homicide *1*
honorary *2*
horsepower *1*
hospitable *2*
hostage *4*
humane *2*
humanity *1*

I
identical *2*
identification *7*
identity *6*
ignite *9*
illegal *1*
immigration *1*
immortal *10*
imperfect *1*
impressive *2*
imprint *6*
improper *1*
impurity *1*
inability *6*
incapable *1*
incense *7*
inequality *11*
infantile *8*
infinite *4*
inflammable *2*
inflate *9*
inflict *2*
infuriate *11*
inhale *5*
initiation *4*
inlaid *2*
inquiry *1*
inscription *2*
inspiration *4*
installment *4*
insulation *7*
integrate *5*
intermediate *10*
intermission *3*
intersection *4*
intoxicate *5*
intrigue *9*
intrude *2*
invasion *2*
invert *2*

invest *5*
investment *8*
isolate *11*

J
jilt *5*
jovial *8*
jubilant *10*
juror *1*
justify *9*
juvenile *3*

L
lavatory *11*
leaflet *10*
lecturer *3*
lessen *5*
lesson *5*
liberal *10*
lisp *10*
literary *11*
locality *6*
logic *8*
logical *2*
lotion *4*
lubricant *1*
lunatic *11*
lyrics *6*

M
maestro *7*
maintenance *4*
maneuver *4*
mangle *8*
maroon *1*
mason *3*
masquerade *10*
massacre *1*
masterpiece *3*
matrimony *4*
maximum *7*
memorandum *6*
midday *4*
mingle *5*
minimum *7*
miscellaneous *2*
mishap *4*
misjudge *5*
mislead *5*

misplace *5*
mobilize *5*
modify *5*
molar *8*
molecule *2*
monastery *1*
morale *10*
morgue *7*
mortgage *11*
motive *3*
multiple *6*
multitude *7*
mutilate *5*
mystify *9*

N
nausea *3*
negative *2*
nomad *11*
nominate *5*
nomination *4*
noticeable *2*
nourish *9*

O
oblong *2*
observatory *7*
occupant *7*
occurrence *7*
ointment *1*
omit *5*
option *3*
outskirts *6*
overcast *8*
overhaul *5*
overlap *5*

P
pacify *11*
pantomime *11*
paralysis *7*
passport *7*
pastel *8*
pasteurize *9*
pawn *8*
pedestrian *3*
penalize *5*
perforate *5*
perpendicular *2*

persistence 8
pharmacy 11
physics 2
piston 1
plaid 11
plaque 1
plasma 3
pneumonia 7
poach 5
pollen 8
pollute 9
portrait 3
possibility 7
postscript 1
precipitation 4
precise 2
predicament 4
prepaid 4
prescribe 4
presciption 4
preview 4
prior 11
privacy 7
probability 6
probe 9
procession 8
proclamation 4
product 11
profile 7
projector 3
prolong 8
propaganda 1
propel 9
proposition 8
proprietor 1
prosperity 4
prosperous 9
proverb 8
provoke 8
pulpit 3
pygmy 3

Q
quake 6
quote 10
quotient 11

R
racial 9

rarity 7
reaction 4
readiness 4
realm 1
recorder 4
recovery 4
recruit 8
reduction 6
reflex 4
refresh 8
registration 3
regrettable 9
rehearsal 3
relapse 8
reliance 6
relish 8
removal 6
renewal 3
repetition 8
reproduce 8
requirement 6
resource 4
respectable 9
respiration 3
restrict 9
resume 5
retain 8
rheumatism 7
rivet 7
ruthless 10

S
Sabbath 3
salve 3
sane 10
sanitation 10
scaly 9
scandal 3
scoff 10
scorch 9
scoundrel 4
Scriptures 3
security 11
senses 9
sensitive 2
sequence 4
serenade 10
sheath 1
shortage 3

shrine 3
shrivel 9
singe 5
singular 2
skyscraper 11
slander 7
solitary 2
soprano 1
specification 6
specify 9
spiritual 10
sponsor 6
spry 10
stanza 1
static 6
sterling 8
stratosphere 1
strenuous 2
strive 5
suffocate 5
suite 5
sullen 10
summary 6
superb 2
surge 10
surgeon 11
surplus 10
survival 7
survivor 6
sweet 5
swerve 10
swindle 10
swivel 5

T
tacked 9
tact 9
tariff 7
temporary 9
testament 3
tracked 5
tract 5
tragedy 11
trait 3
trance 5
trans- 5
transform 8
transmission 1
transmit 8

transplant 1
tuition 8

U
uphold 9
upholster 9
uproar 4

V
vacancy 1
variable 11
variation 6
vat 3
vaudeville 11
ventilate 9
verdict 3
veto 6
via 11
violation 5
vocal 2

Y
yearn 5